# THE
# BURL IVES
# SONG BOOK

# THE
# BURL IVES
# SONG BOOK

## AMERICAN SONG
## IN HISTORICAL PERSPECTIVE

Song Versions by . . . . . . . . . . BURL IVES

Text by . . . . . . . . . . . . . BURL IVES

Arranged for the Piano by . ALBERT HAGUE

Illustrations by . LAMARTINE LE GOULLON
and ROBERT J. LEE

**BALLANTINE BOOKS** • New York

# ACKNOWLEDGMENT

I am not an authority on folk songs in the academic sense, but I have devoted a great part of my life to learning and singing the songs of Great Britain and the United States, songs in the English language. As a professional singer I deliberately chose a large part of my repertoire from these songs.

I learned many of these folk songs as a lad from my parents and my grandparents. In later years, when I had decided that there were songs of folk origin to sing publicly, I worked on most of the major folk song collections. In time, people from all over the world sent me songs that their parents or grandparents had taught them. To all these sources I owe my knowledge of the songs in this book.

It is not possible to acknowledge here the help of all those who have contributed, but among the great song collections I would like to mention the Library of Congress and the University collections of Harvard, Missouri, and Virginia. Among the great individual collectors, I owe a special debt, like all of us who are interested in folk songs, to Carl Sandburg, the Lomaxes, and to the English scholar Cecil Sharpe.

There are as many versions of a folk song as there are people who sing it. These versions are as good or as bad as the taste and ability of the singer. All I can say of the versions in this book is that these are the versions that I sing. The piano accompaniments are designed to supplement the mood and quality of each song.

The songs in this book were seldom meant, in their original form, for piano accompaniment. When I chose Mr. Albert Hague, one of the most talented young musicians of my acquaintance, to make piano arrangements for them, I was certain that he would be faithful to their quality. I feel that he has successfully accomplished this. He has kept the fundamental design of each song, in his own words "tried to capture the nucleus in its simplest form, harmonically, melodically, and rhythmically." He has chosen keys that are easy to play on the piano and kept the range of melody within the limit of the average voice.

And I also must set down my gratitude to my wife, Helen Ives, for organizing and working on the notes with me.

*Burl Ives*

# CONTENTS

# INTRODUCTION

When, as a student of singing, I discovered that there were many beautiful and exciting songs in the English language that nobody sang, that were looked down on as "folk," I chose them for my own. They became my repertoire. I did not sing them because they were folk, but because I thought them musically beautiful and their content meaningful, either dramatically, lyrically, or humorously—always expressive of a genuine human value.

Somewhere along the route, as I came upon the idea that this music was a neglected part of our cultural heritage, I began to organize the songs of our country into chronological sequence. I became aware that the songs might be important, not only musically but historically. A sense of continuity makes a family and a sense of continuity makes a nation one family. What better means is there of knowing ourselves for what we are, and our country for what it is, than devotion to the heritage of pertinent songs the entire nation can sing? And the songs in this book are my selection of songs to sing, out of the vast body of songs that make up our musical heritage.

The periods of our history have been reflected in song. If we examine the songs of the United States from the very beginning, from colonial times to the present, it is possible to get a view of what was sung in the homes, taverns, dining rooms, and concert halls. Such an examination reveals that social and historical events have a parallel body of songs that reflect and describe these happenings, giving us a fresh insight into both sociology and history.

Because folk songs are most often defined as songs whose origin we do not know, and because it will be immediately evident from the notes in this book that we do not know the composers of a great many of the songs that time and usage put in the folk category, I would like to define folk songs as I use the term. As it happens, the question, "What is a folk song?" is the one that I am most frequently asked, so there is need for an answer.

Folk music is difficult to define. Attempts are made to define it by distinguishing it from composed music, classical or popular. Sometimes it is defined in terms of the place where it can be heard . . . only in the home, or at special small gatherings; not in the concert hall, music hall, or on the radio. You will also hear it said that the instruments on which this music is played (the fiddle, the accordion, the harmonica, or the banjo) are nonprofessional instruments.

It is this last statement that leads us in the right direction, because it points out the essential fact that folk music is music played by nonprofessionals. No matter on what instrument it is played, no matter *where* played, *no matter how composed*, folk music defined in terms of its nonprofessional dimensions has individual characteristics imposed by the player, changed by the player.

In other words, no matter what its origin, folk music becomes a part of the *people*, the *folk*, who have molded it and made it their own by imposing their individual and collective mark upon it. This is the *essence . . . a people using music as their own personal expression*. And this is especially true of folk songs, that part of folk music which has interested me.

Now songs are, roughly, of two kinds: "The songs sung at us" (and we enjoy these as a performance) and "the songs sung by us." Of course, these two categories overlap. But it helps us think of what a folk song is, if we say that the folk song is a song sung by us. Thus any song, if taken up by the people of an area and made a part of their singing and musical expression, becomes a folk song.

Yet this is not all that a folk song is. For the entire country will sing a currently popular tune for a few months and then completely forget it. A folk song has to have lasting power. It must convey truth; be a meaningful personal or social or group experience.

You are aware by now that I am not giving you a precise definition of a folk song. But this is the best I can do when I think in terms of both past and present . . . and I must include the present in my definition of the folk song.

A vital people are a singing people, and a vital people have current experiences out of which musical expression must come. This musical expression will become a folk song. This is what folk songs of the past were and are. They are the great bulk of songs created before the days of radio by one or more among a group of people who shared an experience, like pioneering westward or sailing in a clipper ship. It was always a song growing out of the situation . . . sometimes a good song musically, sometimes not. But in every case an honest musical expression taken up by many, and therefore a folk song.

The folk songs in this book are from the past and of the present, your heritage and mine. They are an integral part of the cultural history of the United States. Above all, they are very good songs.

# THE
# BURL IVES
# SONG BOOK

# COLONIAL AMERICA
## 1620-1775

**First Arrivals**—Song has been part of America from the first. Along with their guns, their clothes and basic provisions, the early American settlers brought over their music, sacred and secular.

In England, educated ladies and gentlemen knew how to read music at sight; in each other's homes they would spend evenings singing the madrigals and other music of such composers as Byrd, Weelkes, Dowland, and Morley—everything from simple, lusty songs to intricate counterpoint. Most of the crowd in any tavern could hold their parts in a catch or round. Broadsides, printed ballads on current events, were sold and sung in the streets and were tremendously popular. All this was part of the singing heritage brought over to the New World.

The Ainsworth Psalter was a musical mainstay among the New England colonists. This small psalter brought over by the English Separatists on the *Mayflower* was a book of psalm translations set to simple tunes without harmony by Henry Ainsworth, one of their group, and had been published in 1612 during their stay in Amsterdam. Ainsworth said that since "God's music" for the psalms—Hebrew music—was unknown he felt at liberty to use "man-made tunes."

The first book to be published in America was a book of psalms, printed in Cambridge, Mass., in 1640. There was no music in the book; all the psalms were translated to be sung to well-known hymn tunes of the day. Besides, the preacher usually "lined out" the psalms, chanting them forth line by line with the congregation repeating each line after him. This was *The Bay Psalm Book*.

This psalm book, first sung in the Massachusetts Bay Colony, was not used by the Plymouth Puritans until the end of the century. In the introduction to *The Bay Psalm Book*, the translators explained their efforts: "If the verses are not always so smooth and elegant as some may desire and expect, let them consider that God's altar needs not our polishings, for we have respected rather a plain translation than to smooth our verses with the sweetness of any paraphrase, and so have attended to conscience rather than elegance, and fidelity rather than poetry, in translating Hebrew words into English language, and David's poetry into English metre."

Though the religious influence was strong in New England and emphasis was given to sacred music, still only ten years after the landing of the 1

*Mayflower* printed broadsides describing local events began to appear in the streets. They were mostly in verse and were associated with or written to traditional tunes. These broadsides were very popular in spite of the general tenor of the Bay Colony and in spite of the fulminations of men like Cotton Mather, thundering out against "foolish songs and ballads which hawkers and peddlers carry into all parts of the country."

Benjamin Franklin writes in his *Autobiography* that, early in the eighteenth century, when he was only nine years old:

"My brother put me on composing occasional ballads. One was called the Lighthouse Tragedy; the other was a sailor's song on the taking of Teach (or Blackbeard the Pirate). They were wretched stuff, in the Grub Street ballad style; and when they were printed he sent me about the town to sell them. The first sold wonderfully, the event being recent, having made a great noise. . . ."

In Virginia and the South, a more liberal tradition flourished among the planters and titled settlers. In this sunnier and more easygoing atmosphere, popular ballads and songs were encouraged and the madrigals and traditional songs of old were kept very much alive. In contrast with the New England mood, here is an announcement from the Virginia Gazette of 1737. There were to be horse races and games at a celebration in Hanover County and the paper states further:

"That a Violin be played for by 20 Fiddlers; no person to have the liberty of playing unless he bring a fiddle with him. After the prize is won they are all to play together, and each a different tune, to be treated by the Company. . . . That a handsome entertainment be provided for the subscribers and their wives; and such of them as are not so happy as to have wives may treat any other lady. That Drums, Trumpets, Hautboys, etc., be provided to play at said entertainment. That a quire of ballads be sung for by a number of Songsters, all of them to have liquor sufficient to clear their wind pipes. That a pair of handsome silk of one Pistole value be given to the handsomest Young country maid that appears in the Field. With many other Whimsical and Comical Diversions too numerous to mention."

## America's First Frontier and Its Songs

America's First Frontier and Its Songs—The history of America is the story of the establishment of a series of frontiers, each of which in turn went through several stages until it became a permanent settlement. The first frontier of America was the Eastern Seaboard. As was the case with every frontier, the new settlers brought with them a cultural heritage, including their music and songs.

The songs of the first American frontier were transplanted songs first sung in the British Isles. Since the British were the first settlers to bring their women to this continent, they not only had an advantage in permanent colonization but English became the permanent language of the colonial towns. The colonial mothers taught their children the English language and English songs. Every boat brought over not only current gossip and news from England but whatever was sung at the time. With permanence came newspapers, writers, and, in the tradition of the day, writers of verse ballads about events happening locally. This was the beginning of the writing of songs in the colonies.

Not many songs were written in the colonies during the early period but here and there a colonial activity was recorded in a broadside, put into song form. The French and Indian War, which involved all the colonies, was the first historical event to call forth creative song writing.

There was the song, "Brave Wolfe," about the general who died at the hour of victory in taking Quebec in 1759:

> Brave Wolfe, a gallant youth, did cross the ocean
> To free America from all invasions:
> He landed at Quebec with all his party
> That city to attack, being brave and hearty.
>
> Brave Wolfe drew up his men in a line so pretty
> On the plains of Abraham, before the city:
> A distance from the town the French did meet him
> With double numbers, they resolved to beat him.

After the battle General Wolfe heard that he had defeated Montcalm and that Quebec was his. The last verse of the song runs: "Brave Wolfe replied, 'I die with pleasure.'"

Another song about the French and Indian War was written in 1754 by an officer of the Maryland Independence Company. He composed it to the melody of a current popular English Jacobite song, "Over the Hills and Far Away." The song exhorted:

> Whoe'er is bold, whoe'er is free,
> Will Join and come along with me,
> To drive the French without delay
> Over the hills and far away.
>
> On fair Ohio's bank we stand
> Musket and bayonet in hand
> The French are beat, they dare not stay
> But take to their heels and run away.
>
> Over the rocks and over the steep,
> Over the waters, wide and deep,
> We'll drive the French without delay
> Over the hills and far away.

It is not possible for any song book to include all the important and interesting songs. Therefore you will find the text and music of only two songs from this war included, "Why Soldiers Why?"—a drinking song that was sung during the Revolutionary War, War of 1812, Mexican War, and as late as the Civil War. And, "Yankee Doodle."

This is the most famous song that originated in this war. Its tune was used in ensuing years for many political and social events. It never goes out of fashion. The exact origin of both the tune and the words is the subject of controversy. We know the tune was sung by the Cavaliers in the time of Charles II, to a text which ridiculed two fashionable courtesans of the day:

> Lucy Locket lost her pocket,
> Kitty Fisher found it.
> Not a bit of money in it,
> Only binding round it.

We know the tune was and still is sung in Holland as a harvest song, to doggerel verses that refer to the harvesters' pay: all the buttermilk they could drink and one tenth of the grain they reaped.

> Yanke Dudel, Dodel down,
> Diddle, dudel, lanther,
> Yanke vivor, vover vown,
> Botermilk und tanther.

The word "doodle" refers traditionally to a dull-witted fellow. As for "yankee," one explanation is that the Indians, in trying to pronounce "English," got no closer than "Yengee." Another explanation comes from an officer in General Burgoyne's army, who wrote, "It is derived from a Cherokee word, *eankke*, which signifies coward and slave. This epithet, Yankee, was bestowed upon the residents of New England by Virginians for not assisting them in a war with the Cherokees."

## The Life History of These Songs

The Life History of These Songs — Although each generation preserves from its childhood the songs which the preceding generation has given to it, the songs created in its own generation take precedence. The great-grand-child knows less of his great-grandmother's songs than the grandchild did. In this way, songs that deserve to be remembered in a nation's song heritage can easily disappear.

Until very recently, these songs of colonial America were known only in small areas in isolated parts of our country. They were handed down within a family circle or to a small group. There was no way for them to become known over the whole country; they were not really a part of everyone's heritage or the nation's general culture. The story of their becoming known was first that collectors and researchers became interested in putting these songs in books, or doing scholarly studies of them. As a second stage, many singers became interested in these songs, and then over the radio the songs were heard nationally. Finally, through educational projects in the schools, we find that this musical heritage of America is a part of every school child's experience.

Many of these colonial songs were rediscovered in our Southern Appalachian Mountains by the English folklorist Cecil Sharpe, almost forty years ago. Our own Library of Congress sent out its collectors and they found many versions of the same songs. Harvard and other universities and individual collectors like the Lomaxes have added to this treasury of song. In those parts of the nation where the old Scottish, Irish, Welsh or English songs were not pushed out of singing existence by newer music, these collectors found ten, twenty, and even thirty versions of the same ballad — sometimes with a different tune, sometimes with a different or changed story, but always recognizable and always originating in the same old song. In a few isolated places the ballads were still in existence in what is probably the same form as sung in colonial days. However, we cannot know how the song was sung at that time: there are no recordings to hear and since the songs were transmitted orally, individual variations must have crept in.

The question must be, which versions of these old songs do we sing? Why these versions? And the answer is simple: the best version can only be determined by musical taste. Historically, one is as good and as important as another. But a song is worthy of singing existence not as an historical piece but as an indissoluble welding of poetry and music.

It is my hope that you will find this value in the songs I have chosen, regretting with me that for reasons of space we could not include many more.

# TOBACCO'S BUT AN INDIAN WEED

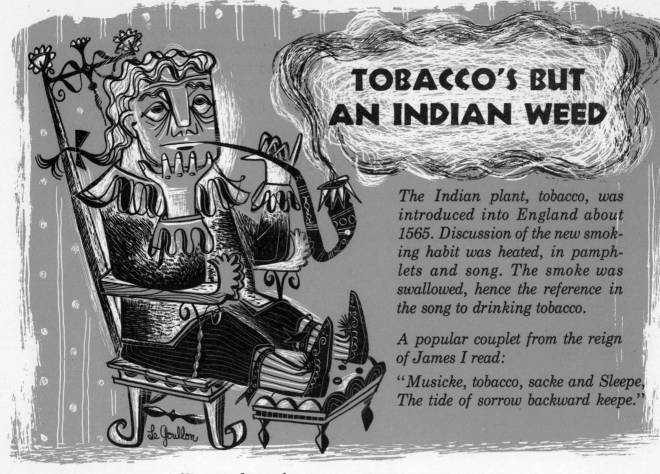

The Indian plant, tobacco, was introduced into England about 1565. Discussion of the new smoking habit was heated, in pamphlets and song. The smoke was swallowed, hence the reference in the song to drinking tobacco.

A popular couplet from the reign of James I read:

"Musicke, tobacco, sacke and Sleepe,
The tide of sorrow backward keepe."

**Firm and steady**

1. To - bac - co's but an In - dian weed, grows green at morn, cut down at eve. It

shows our de-cay:___ we___ are___ but___ clay; think of

this when you smoke to - bac - co.____

2. The pipe that is so lily-white,
    Wherein so many take delight,
        Gone with a touch;
        Man's life is such,
    Think on this, when you smoke tobacco.
3. The pipe that is so foul within,
    Shews how the soul is stained with sin;
        It doth require
        the purging fire.
    Think on this, when you smoke tobacco.
4. The ashes that are left behind,
    Do serve to put us all in mind,
        That unto dust,
        Return we must.
    Think on this, when you smoke tobacco.
5. The smoke that doth so high ascend,
    Shows that our life must have an end;
        The vapour's gone,
        Man's life is done.
    Think on this, when you smoke tobacco.

*Diagrams of the guitar chords used in
this book will be found on pages 301-2.

# LITTLE MOHEE

*This song about the chieftain's only daughter, Mohee, is a beautiful derivation from the bawdy sailor ballad "The Indian Lass."*

1. As I went out walk-ing, _____ up-on a fine day, _____ I got aw-ful lone-some, _____ as the day passed a-way. _____
2. She sat down be-side me _____ and took hold of my hand, _____ said, "You sure be a stran-ger, _____ and in a strange land." _____
3. "My pap-py's a chief-tain, _____ and rul-er be he; _____ I'm his on-ly daugh-ter, _____ and my name is Mo-hee." _____

I sat down a-mus-in',_____ a
She asked me to mar-ry,_____ and
I an-swered and told her_____ that it

lone on the grass,_____ when who should sit by me,—
gave me her hand,_____ said, "My pap-py's a chief-tain—
nev-er could be,_____ 'cause I had my own sweet-heart.

but a sweet In-dian lass._____
all o-ver this land."_____
in my own coun-try._____

4. I had my ain sweetheart and I knew she loved me.
   Her heart was as true as any Mohee.
   So I said, "I must leave you and goodbye my dear,
   There's wind in my canvas and home I must steer."

5. At home with relations I tried for to see,
   But there wasn't a one like my little Mohee;
   And the girl I had trusted proved untrue to me,
   So I sailed o'er the ocean to my little Mohee.

# PSALM III

*In the seventeenth century, the psalms were translated from Latin into well-known ballad meters in the current languages and set to memorable tunes. The Ainsworth Psalter was published in English for the Separatists, a group of whom called themselves Pilgrims and came to America in the Mayflower. Henry Ainsworth translated 39 songs from the Hebrew and set them "To the gravest and easiest tunes of the French and Dutch songs."*

Slow, in 4

*mf*

I laid me down and slept; I wak-ing rose.

For me Je-ho-vah firm-ly up did bear.

For thou-sands ten of folk I will not fear

Which, me be-set-ting, round a-bout en-close.

11.

# CONFESS JEHOVAH

*The Pilgrims, landing at Cape Harbor (Cape Cod), may well have sung this hymn of thankfulness from the Ainsworth Psalter when they "fell upon their knees and blessed ye God in Heaven who had brought ye over ye vast and furious ocean and delivered ye from all perils."*

**In strict rhythm, like a hymn**

1. Con - fess Je - ho - vah thank - ful - ly,
2. To Him that spread the earth more high

for He is good; for His mer - cie
than wa - ters are; for His mer - cie

con - tin - u - eth for - ev - er. To God of gods con - fesse doe ye,
con - tin - u - eth for - ev - er. To Him that made great lights to bee,

be-cause His boun-ti-ful mer-cie    con-tin-u-eth for-ev - er.
be-cause His boun-ti-ful mer-cie    con-tin-u-eth for-ev - er.

Un-to the Lord of lords con-fess, be-cause His mer-ci-ful kind-ness
The sun to have the sove-raign-tie by day, for His be-nigne-mer-cie

con-tin-u-eth for-ev-er.    To Him that doth, Him-self on - ly,
con-tin-u-eth for-ev - er.    The moon and stars for sove-raign-tie

*slower*

things won-drous great; for His mer-cie    con-tin-u-eth for-ev - er.
by night; for His be-nigne-mer-cie    con-tin-u-eth for-ev - er.

*slower*

13.

# OLD HUNDRED

**Definite, but not too slow**

1. All peo-ple that on earth do dwell, sing
2. The Lord, ye know, is God in-deed; with-

to the Lord with cheer-ful voice; Him serve with fear, His
out our aid He did us make; we are His flock, He

praise forth tell; come ye be-fore Him and re - joice.
doth us feed, and for His sheep He doth us take.

*rit.*

14.

3. O enter then His gates with praise,
   Approach with joy His courts unto:
   Praise, laud, and bless His name always,
   For it is seemly so to do.

4. Praise God, from whom all blessings flow;
   Praise Him all creatures here below;
   Praise Him above, ye heav'nly host;
   Praise Father, Son and Holy Ghost.

*This version of the 100th Psalm is first found in the Anglo-Genevan Psalter of 1561. The tune was originally in the French Genevan Psalter set to the 134th Psalm. Typical of Calvinist tunes, it is simple, with only one note to a syllable, and meant for unison singing.*

*Prior to the Reformation only Latin hymns were sung in European churches. After 1551, due to the influence of Luther and Calvin, Swiss, French, German, and English psalters appeared. The vigor and liveliness of these early song tunes, their quick tempo, led them to be called "Geneva Jigs." At the end of the seventeeth century the tunes were deliberately lengthened out to make them more solemn. This is the way we find "Old Hundred" sung today.*

15.

# The Seven Joys of Mary

*Versions of this carol recount Mary's joys in up to 25 verses.*

**Free in delivery**

1. The ver-y first joy that Ma-ry had, it
2. The next good joy that Ma-ry had, it
3. The next good joy that Ma-ry had, it

was the joy of one:— to see her bles-sed Je-sus when
was the joy of two:— to see her own son Je-sus to
was the joy of three:— to see her own son Je-sus to

He was first her son,— when He was first her son.
make the lame to go,— to make the lame to go.
make the blind to see,— to make the blind to see.

16.

CHORUS:

Praise God in the wil-der-ness, and glo - ry be.

Fa-ther, Son, and the Ho-ly Ghost through all e-ter-ni - ty.—

4. The next good joy that Mary had,
   It was the joy of four;
   To see her own son, Jesus Christ
   To read the Bible o'er,
   To read the Bible o'er:
   *Chorus*

5. The next good joy that Mary had,
   It was the joy of five;
   To see her own son, Jesus Christ
   To bring the dead alive,
   To bring the dead alive:
   *Chorus*

6. The next good joy that Mary had,
   It was the joy of six;
   To see her own son, Jesus Christ
   Rise from the Crucifix,
   Rise from the Crucifix:
   *Chorus*

7. The next good joy that Mary had,
   It was the joy of seven;
   To see her own son, Jesus Christ
   To wear the crown of Heaven,
   To wear the crown of Heaven:
   *Chorus*

17.

# THE INDIAN CHRISTMAS CAROL:

**JESUS AHATONIA** *A Jesuit priest wrote this carol, translating the Christmas story into Indian imagery for the Hurons. The French Jesuits often lived with Indian tribes.*

Like a march, not too fast

1. 'Twas in the moon of win-ter-time when all the birds had
2. With-in a lodge of bro-ken bark the ten-der Babe was
3. O chil-dren of the for-est free, o sons of Man - i -

*mf*

Play left hand like a bass drum, but softly.

fled, that might-y Gitch-i - man-i-tou sent
found, a rag-ged robe of rab-bit skin en -
tou, the Ho - ly Child of earth and heav'n is

an - gel choirs in-stead. Be - fore their light the stars grew dim and
wrapped His beau -ty round. The chiefs from far be - fore Him knelt with
born to -day for you. Come kneel be -fore the ra - diant boy who

won-d'ring hunt- ers heard the hymn:—
gifts of fox and bea - ver pelt:— Je-sus, your king, is born,
brings you beau -ty peace and joy.—

Je - sus is born in ex - cel -sis glo - ri - a.

## Hey Diddle Diddle

Easy going

Hey, did-dle, did-dle, the cat and the fid-dle, the cow jumped o-ver the moon; ___ the lit-tle dog laughed to see such sport, and the dish ran a-way with the spoon.

# Fiddle-De-Dee

**Happy, in 2**

Fid-dle-de-dee, fid-dle-de-dee, the fly has mar-ried the bum-ble bee.

**Slower, free in delivery**

1. Says the fly, says he, "Will you mar - ry me? And live with me, sweet bum ble bee?"
2. Said the bee, said she, "I'll live un - der your wing. You'll nev - er know I car - ry a sting."
3. So when par - son bee - tle joined the pair, they both went out to take the air.
4. Oh, the flies did buzz and the bells did ring. Did you ev - er hear so mer - ry a thing?

*Like many colonial mothers, Mrs. Elizabeth Goose of Boston entertained her grandchildren with nursery songs from England, of which she knew an amazing number. Her son-in-law, Tom Fleet, printed and thus preserved these songs in a collection entitled: SONGS FOR THE NURSERY OR MOTHER GOOSE MELODIES FOR CHILDREN (1719).*

# Mr. Froggie Went A-Courting

*This is one of the oldest and most popular narrative animal songs for children in the English language. It first occurs in a Scottish broadside, 1549, "The Frog Came to the Myl Dur" (mill door).*

With a happy beat

1. Mis-ter Frog-gie went a-court-ing, and he did ride, mm - mm, _____ Mis-ter Frog-gie went a-court-ing, and he did ride, a
2. He went down to Mis-sy Mous-y's door, mm - mm, _____ He went down to Mis-sy Mous-y's door, where

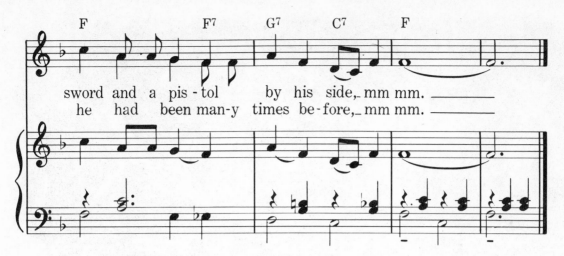

sword and a pis - tol   by his side,_ mm mm. _____
he   had   been man-y   times be - fore,_ mm mm. _____

3. "Mis-sy Mous-ey are you within, mm-mm,
   Mis-sy Mous-ey are you within?"
   "Yes kind sir, I sit and spin," mm-mm.

4. He took Missy Mouse upon his knee, mm-mm,
   Took Missy Mouse upon his knee,
   Said "Missy Mouse, will you marry me?" mm-mm.

5. "Without my Uncle Rat's consent, mm-mm,
   Without my Uncle Rat's consent,
   I wouldn't marry the Pres-I-dent," mm-mm.

6. Uncle Rat laughed and shook his fat sides, mm-mm,
   Uncle Rat laughed and shook his fat sides,
   To think his niece would be a bride, mm-mm.

7. When Uncle Rat gave his consent, mm-mm,
   When Uncle Rat gave his consent,
   The weasel wrote the publishment, mm-mm.

8. Next came in was a bumblebee, mm-mm,
   Next came in was a bumblebee,
   Danced a jig with a two-legged flea, mm-mm.

9. The owl did hoot, the birds they sang, mm-mm,
   The owl did hoot, the birds they sang,
   And through the woods the music rang, mm-mm.

10. Where will the wedding breakfast be, mm-mm,
    Where will the wedding breakfast be?
    Way down yonder in a hollow tree, mm-mm.

11. What will the wedding breakfast be, mm-mm,
    What will the wedding breakfast be?
    Two green beans and a black-eyed pea, mm-mm.

12. They all went sailing across the lake, mm-mm,
    All went sailing across the lake,
    And got swallowed up by a big, black snake, mm-mm.

13. There's bread and cheese upon the shelf, mm-mm,
    There's bread and cheese upon the shelf,
    If you want any more, you can sing it yourself, mm-mm.

# The Tailor and the Mouse

*Another children's favorite with nonsense syllables,*
*which occur frequently from the fifteenth century on.*

Lively, in 2

There was a tai-lor had a mouse, Hi-did-dle dum cum
The tai-lor had a tall silk hat, Hi-did-dle dum cum
The tai-lor he chased him o-ver the lea, Hi-did-dle dum cum

feed-a They lived to - geth-er in one house.
feed-a The mouse he ate it, fan-cy that.
feed-a The last of that mouse he never did see.

24.

25.

# THE FOX

Lively

1. Fox went out on a chil-ly night,
(2.) ran till he came to a great big bin, where the
(3.) grabbed the gray goose by the neck,

prayed for the moon for to give him light, for he'd
ducks and the geese were put there-in. "A
throwed a duck a-cross his back.

man-y a mile to go that night a-fore he reached the
cou-ple of you will grease my chin a-fore I leave this
He did-n't mind their quack, quack, quack, and their legs all dan-gling

town-o,       town-o,  town-o,      he'd man-y a mile to
town-o,       town-o,  town-o,      a cou-ple of you will
down-o,       down-o,  down-o,      he did-n't  mind their

go     that     night    a - fore   he    reached the
grease  my     chin     a - fore   I     leave   this
quack, quack,   quack, with their    legs   all    dan - gling

town - o. _____ 2. He —
town - o. _____ 3. He
down - o. _____

27.

# THE FOX

4. Then old mother Flipper-Flopper jumped out of bed,
   Out of the window she cocked her head,
   Crying, "John! John! The grey goose is gone
      And the fox is on the town-o,
         Town-o, town-o!"
   Crying, "John! John! The grey goose is gone,
      And the fox is on the town-o!"

5. Then John, he went to the top of the hill,
   Blowed his horn both loud and shrill;
   The fox, he said, "I better flee with my kill
      Or they'll soon be on my trail-o,
         Trail-o, trail-o."
   Fox, he said, "I better flee with my kill,
      Or they'll soon be on my trail-o."

6. He ran till he came to his cozy den,
   There were the little ones eight, nine, ten.
   They said, "Daddy, better go back again,
      'Cause it must be a mighty fine town-o,
         Town-o, town-o,"
   They said, "Daddy, better go back again,
      'Cause it must be a mighty fine town-o."

7. Then the fox and his wife without any strife,
   Cut up the goose with a fork and knife;
   They never had such a supper in their life
      And the little ones chewed on the bones-o,
         Bones-o, bones-o.
   They never had such a supper in their life
      And the little ones chewed on the bones-o.

# THE ESCAPE OF
# OLD JOHN WEBB

*Only religious songs were approved in the New England colonies. However, ballads on current happenings could not be suppressed and broadsides describing events often took the place of newspapers. The broadsides were accounts in verse associated with or written to traditional tunes. About the year 1730, John Webb and Bill Tenor were imprisoned at Salem, Mass. Their imprisonment was unpopular. The jail raid which freed them was much applauded and a twenty-verse broadside was printed describing the incident.*

29.

# THE ESCAPE OF OLD JOHN WEBB

*This song, madrigal in form, was composed from the broadside. Government authorities advertised unsuccessfully for information regarding author and printer.*

Definite, in 4

1. There were nine to guard the Brit - ish ranks and
There was eight - y weight of good Span-ish iron be -
2. They mount-ed their horse and a - way did ride (and
And then they called for a room to dance (and

five to guard the town a - bout, _____ and
tween his neck - bone and his knee, _____ but
who but they rode gal - lant - ly), _____ un -
who but they danced mer - ri - ly), _____ and

two to _____ stand at _____ ei - ther hand, and
Bil - ly took John-ny up un-der his arm and
til they _____ came to the riv - er bank, and
the best danc - er a - mong them all was

3

one to let old ___ ten - or out. ___
lugged him a - way right ___ art - ful - ly. ___
there they a - light-ed right ___ mer - ri - ly. ___
old John Webb who was just set free. ___

And

CHORUS:

Bil-ly broke locks, and Bil-ly broke bolts, and Bil-ly broke all that

he came nigh, _____ un - til he __ came to the

dun-geon door, and that he broke right man - ful - ly. ___

3

31.

# THREE ROUNDS

*Part singing was general in England in the seventeenth and eighteenth centuries. Lords and ladies, tinkers and blacksmiths, all were used to singing in parts. Catches and rounds were particularly in favor since each person sang the same notes and the music was easy to remember.*

## THE HART HE LOVES THE HIGH WOOD

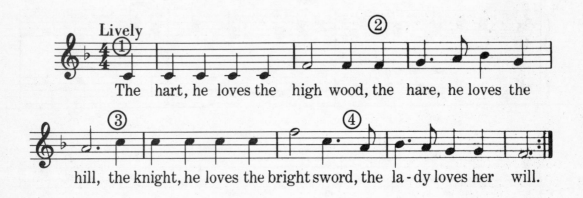

The hart, he loves the high wood, the hare, he loves the hill, the knight, he loves the bright sword, the la-dy loves her will.

## OH, ABSALOM, MY SON

Oh, Ab - sa - lom, my son, my son, oh, Ab - sa - lom, my son, my son, would to God ___ I had died for thee,_ my_ son, would to God ___ I had **died for**

thee, my son. Oh, Ab - sa - lom, my son, — my —
son, oh, Ab - sa - lom, my son, my son.

## LET SIMON'S BEARD ALONE

With dignity

Let Si - mon's beard a - lone, a - lone, let — Si - mon's beard a -

lone; — 'Tis no dis - grace to Si - mon's face, for —

he had nev - er one; — Then mock not, nor scoff not, nor

jeer not, nor sneer not, but rath - er him be - moan. —

# GREENSLEEVES

*A diary of 1596 mentions "Greensleeves" as a dance to which a young lass "was footing it aloft on the green, with foot out, and foot in." Falstaff, in "The Merry Wives of Windsor" rants, "Let the skies rain potatoes, Let it thunder to the tune of Greensleeves."*

CHORUS:

Green - sleeves was__ all my joy,_____
Green - sleeves was__ my de-light. Green - sleeves was my
heart of gold, and__ who but La - dy__ Green - sleeves.

35.

4. I bought thee petticoats of the best,
   The cloth so fine as might be;
   I gave thee jewels for thy chest,
   And all this cost I spent on thee. *Chorus:*

5. Thy smock of silk, both fair and white,
   With gold embroidered gorgeously;
   Thy petticoat of sendal right,*
   And these I bought thee gladly. *Chorus:*

6. They set thee up, they took thee down,
   They served thee with humility;
   Thy foot might not once touch the ground,
   And yet thou wouldst not love me. *Chorus:*

7. Well I will pray to God on high,
   That thou my constancy mayst see,
   And that yet once before I die
   Thou wilt vouchsafe to love me. *Chorus:*

8. Greensleeves, now farewell! adieu!
   God I pray to prosper thee!
   For I am still thy lover true,
   Come once again and love me. *Chorus:*
   *Thin silk

*My Lady Greensleeves dressed elegantly. Regarding women's clothes in the colonies, Nathaniel Ward wrote in the mid-seventeenth century: "To speak moderately, I truly confess it is beyond the ken of my understanding to conceive how those women should have any true grace or valuable virtue that have so little wit as to disfigure themselves with such exotic garb, as not only dismantles their native lovely lustre but transclouts them into gantbar-geese, ill-shapen-shotten shellfish, Egyptian hieroglyphics, or at the best into French flirts of the pastry, which a proper English woman should scorn with her heels."*

# 'Tis Women

Canon  4 voices

Henry Purcell
(1659–95)

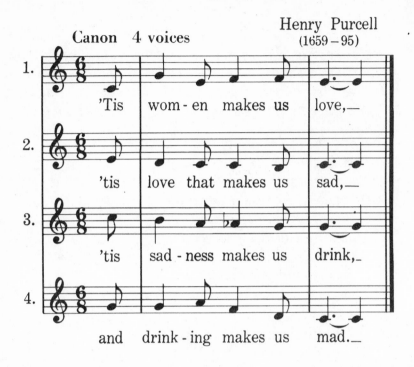

1. 'Tis wom-en makes us love,—

2. 'tis love that makes us sad,—

3. 'tis sad-ness makes us drink,—

4. and drink-ing makes us mad.—

# THE RIDDLE SONG

*Unlike this short form, traditional riddle songs had a story setting. Usually a knight offers to marry the youngest of three sisters if her word equals her beauty. She answers the first three questions in verse one below. The song goes:*

*When she these questions answered had*
*The knight became exceeding glad*
*And after that 'tis verified*
*He made of her his lovely bride.*
*So now fair maids, all adieu,*
*This song I dedicate to you,*
*And wish you thus may constant prove*
*Unto the man you do love.*

**Gentle (rhythm only softly indicated)**

1. I gave my love a cher-ry that has no stone. I
2. How can there be a cher-ry that has no stone? How
3. A cher-ry when it's bloom-in' it has no stone. A

gave my love a chick-en that has no bone. I
can there be a chick-en that has no bone? How
chick-en when it's peep-in' it has no bone. A

# THE DEVIL'S NINE QUESTIONS

*Mummer's dances that pictured the devil trying to win a soul
were done to a singing dialogue of which this is an example.*

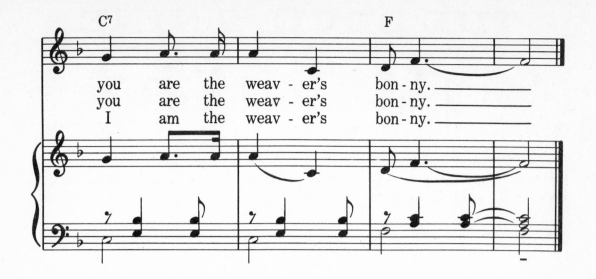

you       are    the    weav - er's    bon - ny. _____
you       are    the    weav - er's    bon - ny. _____
I       am    the    weav - er's    bon - ny. _____

4. What is higher than a tree?
Sing ninety-nine and ninety.
And what is deeper than the sea?
And you are the weaver's bonny.

    5. Heaven is higher than a tree
      Sing ninety-nine and ninety.
      And Hell is deeper than the sea
      And I am the weaver's bonny.

6. What is louder than a horn?
Sing ninety-nine and ninety.
And what is sharper than a thorn?
And you are the weaver's bonny.

    7. Thunder is louder than a horn
      Sing ninety-nine and ninety.
      Death is sharper than a thorn
      And I am the weaver's bonny.

8. What's more innocent than a lamb?
Sing ninety-nine and ninety.
And what is meaner than womankind?
And you are the weaver's bonny.

    9. A babe's more innocent than a lamb
      Sing ninety-nine and ninety.
      She-devil is meaner than womankind
      And I am the weaver's bonny.

10. You have answered my questions nine
Sing ninety-nine and ninety.
You are God's own and none of mine
And you are the weaver's bonny.

# Paper of Pins

*An Americanized version of an English courtship game, "The Keys of Canterbury," to be both sung and acted out.*

**Steady, in 2**

I'll give to you a pa-per of pins, and that's the way our love be-gins, If you will mar-ry me, me, me, if you will mar-ry me.

2. I'll not accept a paper of pins
    If that's the way that love begins
        And I won't marry you, you, you;
        And I won't marry you.

3. I'll give to you a little lap dog
    To carry with you when you go abroad
        If you will marry me, me, me;
        If you will marry me.

4. I'll not accept a little dog
    To carry with me when I go abroad
        And I won't marry you, you, you;
        And I won't marry you.

5. I'll give you a house and land,
    Twenty-five cattle and one hired man,
        If you will marry me, me, me;
        If you will marry me.

6. I'll not accept your house and land,
    Twenty-five cattle and one hired man,
        Oh, I'll not marry you, you, you;
        I'll not marry you.

7. I'll give to you a dress of red,
    Stitched all around with golden thread,
        If you will marry me, me, me;
        If you will marry me.

8. I'll not accept your dress of red,
    Stitched all around with golden thread,
        I'll not marry you, you, you;
        I'll not marry you.

9. I'll give to you a key to my chest
    And all the money that I possess,
        If you will marry me, me, me;
        If you will marry me.

10. Yes, I'll accept the key to your chest
    And all the money that you possess,
        Yes, yes, I'll marry you, you, you;
        Yes, I will marry you.

11. Ha, ha, ha, money is all,
    A woman's love is nothing at all;
        No, I'll not marry you, you, you;
        No, I'll not marry you.

# THE GOLDEN VANITY

*This early ballad was first printed as "Sir Walter Raleigh Sailing in the Lowlands, showing how the famous ship* The Sweet Trinity *was taken by a false galley; and how it was recovered by the craft of the Little Sea-boy who sunk the galley." The Roxburg Ballads comment on the song: "Raleigh really was deemed arrogant, selfish, with the airs of an upstart, insolent to superiors, unconciliating with equals and heartlessly indifferent to those in low position. The subject of the ballad is fictitious— sheer invention of course. The selfishness and ingratitude displayed by Raleigh agreed with the current estimate."*

With feeling

1. There was a ship that sailed _____ all on the Low-land sea, and the name of our ship was the

2. Then up stepped our cab-in boy, and bold-ly out-spoke he, and he said to our cap-tain, "What

44.

Gold - en Van - i - ty, and we feared she would be tak- en by the
would you give to me, if I would swim a - long side of the

Span - ish en - e - my as she sailed in the Low-land,
Span - ish en - e - my, and __ sink her in the Low-land,

Low - land, Low, as she sailed in the Low-land sea.
Low - land, Low, and sink her in the Low-land sea?"

*slower*

*a tempo*

# THE GOLDEN VANITY

3. "Oh, I would give you silver, and I would give you gold,
   And my own fairest daughter your bonny bride shall be,
   If you will swim alongside of the Spanish enemy
   And sink her in the lowland, lowland, low,
   And sink her in the lowland sea."

4. Then the boy he made him ready and overboard sprang he,
   And he swam alongside of the Spanish enemy,
   And with his brace and auger in her side he bored holes three,
   And he sunk her in the lowland, lowland, low,
   Yes, he sunk her in the lowland sea.

5. Then quickly he swam back to the cheering of the crew,
   But the captain would not heed him, for his promise he did rue,
   And he scorned his poor entreatings when loudly he did sue,
   And he left him in the lowland, lowland, low,
   And he left him in the lowland sea.

6. Then quickly he swam round to the port side,
   And up unto his messmates full bitterly he cried,
   "Oh, messmates, draw me up, for I'm drifting with the tide,
   And I'm sinking in the lowland, lowland, low,
   I'm sinking in the lowland sea."

7. Then his messmates drew him up, but on the deck he died,
   And they stitched him in his hammock which was so fair and wide,
   And they lowered him overboard and he drifted with the tide,
   And he sank in the lowland, lowland, low,
   And he sank in the lowland sea.

# Captain Kidd or

## HOW A BROADSIDE BALLAD BROUGHT A PIRATE TO THE GALLOWS

*Freebooting waged against the enemies of England was Privateering and was initiated and condoned by other governments as well. Any ship on the sea might carry a commission from England, France, Holland, or Spain to seize enemy or neutral vessels as legal prize. Freebooting that preyed on ships carrying cargoes or passengers between England and her colonies without such a commission, or for private gain, was considered pirate and criminal.*

*This is what happened to Captain Kidd, who began as a privateer from New York City.*

*The pirates had been making such inroads on English colonial shipping that King William and several colonial governors formed a stock company to hunt them down and incidentally to capture and sell the pirate vessels for a profit. To command their vessel, The Adventure Galley, they hired Captain Kidd.*

*Captain Kidd cruised the American coast looking for pirates without success. His crew, who were to participate in profits, became mutinous and demanded action. Kidd agreed to attack French and other ships, at that time fair game for Englishmen. Unfortunately Kidd became notorious which proved politically inconvenient to his employers, especially the King, who was then negotiating a truce with France. Kidd was haled to England on a trumped-up charge of murdering his gunner, whom he had accidentally killed.*

47.

## CAPTAIN KIDD

*Popular sentiment was directed against him by a ballad purporting to tell the story of his evil deeds as a pirate. As a contemporary put it, Captain Kidd was hanged "by a doggerel ballad sung to a villainous tune." Actually the tune proved very singable and several hymns have been written to its insistent dirge-like strains.*

Medium, in 2

1. Oh, my name was Wil-liam Kidd, as I sailed, as I
2. Oh, my par-ents taught me well, as I sailed, as I
3. Oh, I mur-dered Wil-liam Moore, as I sailed, as I

sailed, my name was Wil-liam Kidd, as I sailed,— my
sailed, my par-ents taught me well, as I sailed,— my
sailed, I mur-dered Wil-liam Moore, as I sailed,— I—

name was Wil-liam Kidd, God's laws I did for-bid, and most
par-ents taught me well, to— shun the gates of hell, but a-
mur-dered Wil-liam Moore, and I left him in his gore, not—

48.

wick - ed - ly  I  did,  as  I  sailed,  as  I  sailed.
gainst them I  re - belled, as  I  sailed,  as  I  sailed.
man - y leagues from shore, as  I  sailed,  as  I  sailed.

4. Oh I steered from sound to sound, as I sailed, as I sailed,
Oh I steered from sound to sound, as I sailed.
I steered from sound to sound, and many ships I found,
And all of them I burned, as I sailed, as I sailed,
And all of them I burned as I sailed.

5. And being cruel still, as I sailed, as I sailed,
And being cruel still as I sailed,
And being cruel still, my gunner I did kill,
And his precious blood did spill, as I sailed, as I sailed,
And his precious blood did spill, as I sailed.

6. I was sick and nigh to death, as I sailed, as I sailed,
I was sick and nigh to death as I sailed.
I was sick and nigh to death and I vowed with every breath,
To walk in wisdom's ways, when I sailed, when I sailed,
To walk in wisdom's ways when I sailed.

7. My repentance lasted not, as I sailed, as I sailed,
My repentance lasted not, as I sailed.
My repentance lasted not, my vows I soon forgot,
Damnation was my lot, as I sailed, as I sailed,
Damnation was my lot as I sailed.

8. To the execution dock I must go, I must go,
To the execution dock I must go.
To the execution dock, while many thousands flock,
But I must bear the shock and must die, and must die,
But I must bear the shock and must die.

9. Take a warning now by me, for I must die, for I must die,
Take a warning now by me for I must die.
Take a warning now by me and shun bad company,
Lest you come to hell with me, for I must die, I must die,
Lest you come to hell with me, for I must die.

# Henry Martin

*This ballad is based on the true story of Andrew Barton, who commanded an English merchantman taken by the Portuguese in 1476. His three sons were granted letters of reprisal by the king, but Andrew Barton (Henry Martin) seized English goods as well as Portuguese. This piracy was put down by the king's ship* The Lion, *which captured the ambitious Andrew.*

**Waltz**

There were three broth-ers in mer-ry Scot-land, in mer-ry Scot-land there were three;_____ and they did cast lots which of them__ should go,__ should

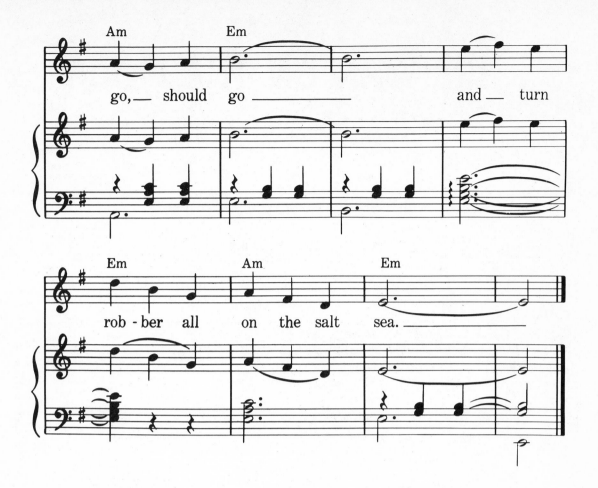

go,— should go _____ and — turn

rob - ber all on the salt sea. _____

2. The lot it fell upon Henry Martin,
The youngest of all the three,
That he should turn robber all on
      the salt sea, etc.
For to maintain his two brothers
      and he.

3. He had not been sailing but a long
      Winter's night,
Part of a short Winter's day,
Before he espied a stout lofty ship, etc.
Come a-riding down on him straight-way.

4. "Hello, hello," cried Henry Martin,
"What makes you sail so nigh?"
"I'm a rich merchant ship bound for
      fair London town, etc.
Will you please for to let me pass by?"

5. "Oh no, oh no," cried Henry Martin,
"That thing it never can be,
For I have turned robber all on the
      salt sea, etc.
For to maintain my two brothers and me."

6. "Then lower your topsail and bow
      down your mizzen,
Bow yourselves under my lee,
Or I shall give to you a fast-
      flowing ball, etc.
And cast your dear bodies down in the
      salt sea."

7. With broadside and broadside and
      at it they went,
For fully two hours or three,
'Til Henry Martin give to her the
      death shot, etc.
And straight to the bottom went she.

8. Bad news, bad news to old
      England came,
Bad news to old London town,
There's been a rich vessel and
      she's cast away, etc.
And all of her merry men drowned.

# BRENNAN ON THE MOOR

*The ballad of Brennan, the Robin Hood of the Irish scene,*
*was current in Ireland, Scotland, and the colonies in the*
*seventeenth and eighteenth centuries.*

Free in delivery, with mounting excitement

1. It's a - bout a fierce high-way man my sto - ry I will
2. It was up - on the King's high-way old Bren-nan he sat

tell. His name was Wil - ly Bren - nan, and in
down. He met the mayor of Moor - land five

Ire - land he did dwell. 'Twas up - on the King's__
miles out - side of town. Now the May - or, he knew

moun-tain he be-gan his wild ca-reer, and
Bren-nan, and, "I think," says he, "your

Am                                    C

man-y a rich gen-tle-man be-fore him shook with fear. Oh, it's
name is Wil-ly Bren-nan, you must come a-long with me." Oh, it's

Am            Em            Am

CHORUS: steady, like a dirge

C                              Em

Bren-nan on the moor, Bren-nan on the moor,

slower C                              F            C

bold, gay, and un-daunt-ed stood young Bren-nan on the moor.

slower

53.

3. Now Brennan's wife was a-going down town
   Some provisions for to buy.
   When she saw her Willy taken
   She began to weep and cry.
   Says he, "Hand me that ten penny,"
   And as soon as Willy spoke
   She handed him a blunderbuss
   From underneath her cloak.
   *Chorus*

4. Now Brennan got his blunderbuss,
   My story I'll unfold.
   He caused the mayor to tremble
   And to deliver up his gold.
   Five thousand pounds were offered
   For his apprehension there,
   But Brennan and the pedlar
   To the mountain did repair.
   *Chorus*

5. Now Brennan is an outlaw
   All on some mountain high.
   With infantry and cavalry
   To take him they did try,
   But he laughed at them and he scorned at them
   Until it was said
   By a false-hearted woman
   He was cruelly betrayed.
   *Chorus*

6. They hung Brennan at the crossroads;
   In chains he swung and dried.
   But still they say that in the night
   Some do see him ride.
   They see him with his blunderbuss
   In the midnight chill;
   Along, along the King's highway
   Rides Willy Brennan still.
   *Chorus*

# EDWARD

*Because of geographic isolation, Americanized versions of old British ballads were sung in the southern Appalachian Mountains until the radio supplanted them with popular and hillbilly music. This ballad, like the other narrative ballads that follow, was collected by Cecil Sharpe, the English folk-song collector, in 1914.*

**Melancholy, but with motion**

1. What makes that blood on the point of your knife? My son, now tell to me.— It is the blood of my
2. It is too red for your old gray mare, my son, now tell to me.— It is the blood of my
3. It is too red for your old coon dog, my son, now tell to me.— It is the blood of my

old _ gray mare who plowed the fields _ for
old _ coon dog who chased the fox __ for
broth - er John who hoed the corn _ for

*soft rhythm*

me, me, me, who plowed the fields for me.
me, me, me, who chased the fox _ for me.
me, me, me, who hoed the corn for me.

*slower*

*slower*

*p*

*r.h.*

4. What did you fall out about, my own dear son?
   My son, now tell to me.
   Because he cut yon holly bush
   Which might have been a tree, tree, tree,
   Which might have been a tree.

5. What will you say when your father comes home,
   When he comes home from town?
   I'll set my foot in yonder boat,
   And I'll sail the ocean round, round, round,
   I'll sail the ocean round.

6. When will you come back, my own dear son?
   My son, now tell to me.
   When the sun it sets in yonder sycamore tree,
   And that will never be, be, be,
   And that will never be.

# Barbara Allen

*Some version of Barbara Allen is found wherever the English language is spoken. There are versions in broadsides and song-book collections as far back as we know of songs so recorded. It is the most popular classic ballad of the western world, and both its melody and its story are found from Italy to the Scandinavian countries.*

**Plaintive (free in delivery)**

1. In Scar-let town_____ where I was born,____ there was a fair maid dwell-in',_____ made ev'ry youth____ cry well - a - day, and her

2. 'Twas in the mer - ry, mer-ry month of May,____ when green buds they were swell-in';_____ sweet Wil-liam on____ his death - bed lay for the

name     was    Bar - b'ry    Al - len._____
love    of    Bar - b'ry    Al - len._____

3. He sent his servant to the town,
   To the place where she was a-dwellin',
   Cried, "Master bids you come to him,
   If your name be Barb'ry Allen."

4. Then slowly, slowly she got up,
   And slowly went she nigh him,
   And when she pulled the curtains back
   Said, "Young man, I think you're dyin'."

5. "Oh, yes, I'm sick, I'm very very sick,
   And I never will be better,
   Until I have the love of one,
   The love of Barb'ry Allen."

6. "Oh, ken ye not in yonder town
   In the place where you were a-dwellin',
   You gave a toast to the ladies all
   But you slighted Barb'ry Allen."

7. "Oh yes, I ken, I ken it well,
   In the place where I was a-dwellin';
   I give a toast to the ladies all,
   But my love to Barb'ry Allen."

8. Then lightly tripped she down the stairs,
   He trembled like an aspen.
   'Tis vain, 'tis vain, my dear young man,
   To hone for Barb'ry Allen.

9. She walkéd out in the green, green fields.
   She heard his death bells knellin'.
   And every stroke they seemed to say,
   "Hard-hearted Barb'ry Allen."

10. Her eyes looked east, her eyes looked west,
    She saw his pale corpse comin';
    She cried, "Bearers, bearers, put him down
    That I may look upon him."

11. The more she looked, the more she grieved,
    Until she burst out cryin';
    She cried, "Bearers, bearers, take him off,
    For I am now a-dyin'!"

12. "Oh, father, oh, father, go dig my grave,
    Go dig it deep and narrow.
    Sweet William died for me today;
    I'll die for him tomorrow."

13. They buried her in the old churchyard,
    Sweet William's grave was nigh her,
    And from his heart grew a red, red rose,
    And from her heart a brier.

14. They grew and they grew o'er the old church wall,
    Till they couldn't grow no higher,
    Until they tied a true lover's knot,
    The red rose and the brier.

59.

# Lord Randall

*This Scottish ballad came over with 7,000 followers of Bonnie Prince Charlie settling North Carolina after his defeat in 1745.*

Very free in delivery

1. Where have you been all the day, Ran-dall, my son?
2. What have you been eat-ing there, Ran-dall, my son?
3. Where did she get them from, Ran-dall, my son?

Play all chords as arpeggios.

Where have you been all the day, my pret-ty one? I've
What have you been eat-ing there, my pret-ty one? ___
Where did she get them from, my pret-ty one? From

been to my sweet-heart's, Moth-er, I've been to my
Eels and eel broth, Moth-er, ___ eels and
hedg-es and ditch-es, Moth-er, from hedg-es and

sweet-heart's, —— Moth-er;
eel broth, —— Moth-er; Make my bed soon, for I'm
ditch - es, —— Moth-er;

sick to my heart, and I fain would lie down.

4. What was the color of their skins, Randall, my son?
What was the color of their skins, my pretty one?
Spickled and spackled, Mother,
Spickled and spackled, Mother;
Make my bed soon, for I'm sick to my heart, and I fain would lie down.

5. What will you leave your brother, Randall, my son?
What will you leave your brother, my pretty one?
My gold and silver, Mother,
My gold and silver, Mother;
Make my bed soon, for I'm sick to my heart, and I fain would lie down.

6. What will you leave your sweetheart, Randall, my son?
What will you leave your sweetheart, my pretty one?
A rope to hang her, Mother,
A rope to hang her, Mother;
Make my bed soon, for I'm sick to my heart, and I fain would lie down.

# Lord Thomas and Fair Elinore

*Also familiar as "The Brown Girl," this bloody ballad is second only to "Barb'ry Allen" in universal popularity.*

Waltz, steady rhythm

1. Lord Thom-as rose ear-ly one morn-ing in May and dress'd him-self __ in blue, _____ say-ing, "Moth-er, I'm go-in' to get mar-ried to-

2. "The brown girl has house __ and land, fair El-i-nore, she __ has none." _____ "There-fore __ I charge you with my

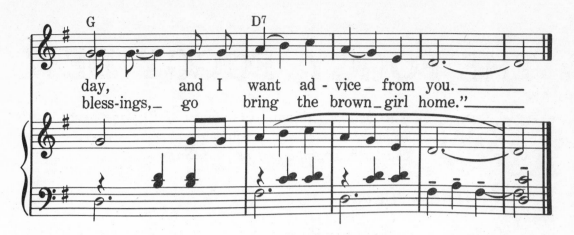

day,  and I want ad - vice _ from you. _____
bless-ings, _ go  bring the brown _ girl home." _____

3. He rode 'til he came to fair
  Elinore's gate,
Rattled at the ring;
There was no one more ready than she
To arise and let him in.

4. "What's the matter, Lord Thomas?"
  she cried,
"What's the matter with you?"
"I've come to invite you to my wedding.
Ain't that good news to you?"

5. "Oh, mother, shall I go to
  Lord Thomas's weddin',
Or shall I tarry at home?"
"Therefore, I charge you with my
  blessings,
You'd better tarry at home."

6. She dressed herself in her best
And most of her dressings were green,
And every village that she rode through,
They took her to be some queen.

7. She rode 'til she came to
  Lord Thomas's gate
Rattled at the ring;
There was no one more ready than he
To arise and let her in.

8. He took her by the lily white hand
And led her in the hall,
And seated her there at the head
  of the table
Amongst the gentlemen all.

9. "Is this your bride, sits here
  by your side?
I'm sure she's wonderful brown.
You might have married as fine
  a young lady
As ever the sun shone on."

10. The brown girl, she had a knife.
It was both long and sharp.
She pierced it into fair Elinore's side,
And it entered into her heart.

11. "What's the matter, fair Elinore?"
  he cried,
"What's the matter with you?"
"Oh, don't you see my own heart's blood
A-trickling down my side?"

12. He took the brown girl by the hand
And led her in the hall;
And there with a sword cut off her head
And dashed it against the wall.

13. Saying, "Here's the death of three
  true lovers,
God send their souls to rest;
And bury the brown girl at my feet
And fair Elinore at my breast."

# THE FOGGY, FOGGY DEW

*This ballad, still sung in the west of England today, exists in many American versions . . . some suggestive, some chaste. It originally stems from Suffolk.*

**Free in delivery**

1. When I was a bach-'lor, I lived all a-lone, I worked at the weav-er's trade; and the on-ly, on-ly thing that I did that was wrong, was to woo a fair young maid. I

2. One night she knelt close by my side when I was fast a-sleep. she threw her arms a-round my neck, and then be-gan to weep. She

**Slow rhythm, in 4**

wooed her in the win-ter-time, part of the sum-mer,
wept, she cried, she tore her hair, ah, me! what could I

*a little faster*

too; and the on-ly, on-ly thing that I did
do? So all night long I

*a little faster*

that was wrong, was to keep her from the fog-gy, fog-gy dew.
held her in my arms, just to keep her from the fog-gy, fog-gy dew.

3. Again I am a bachelor, I live with my son,
   We work at the weaver's trade;
   And every single time that I look into his eyes,
   He reminds me of the fair young maid.
   He reminds me of the wintertime,
   Part of the summer, too,
   And of the many, many times that I held her in my arms,
   Just to keep her from the foggy, foggy dew.

# PRETTY POLLY

*An English broadside ballad entitled "The Gosport Trag-edy" was current in both England and the colonies in 1710. The subject matter was an oft-repeated one in ballads. It was the story of a sailor who stabs his mistress when she is about to become a mother. In the early version the sailor flees aboard ship where he is confronted by her ghost.*

**With a steady beat**

I court-ed pret-ty Pol - ly the live - long—

night, I court-ed pret-ty Pol - ly the live - long

66.

night, then left her next morn-ing be-fore it was light.

2. "Pretty Polly, pretty Polly, come go along with me,
   Pretty Polly, pretty Polly, come go along with me
   Before we get married some pleasures to see."

3. She jumped on behind him and away they did go;
   She jumped on behind him and away they did go
   Over the hills and the valley below.

4. They went a little further and what did they spy;
   They went a little further and what did they spy,
   A new dug grave with a spade laying by.

5. "Oh, Willie, oh, Willie, I'm 'fraid of your way;
   Oh, Willie, oh, Willie, I'm 'fraid of your way;
   I'm afraid you will lead my poor body astray."

6. "Pretty Polly, pretty Polly, you've guessed about right;
   Pretty Polly, pretty Polly, you've guessed about right;
   For I slept on your grave the best part of last night."

7. He throwed her on the ground and she broke into tears;
   He throwed her on the ground and she broke into tears;
   She throwed her arms around him and trembled with fear.

8. There's no time to talk now, there's no time to stand;
   There's no time to talk now, there's no time to stand;
   He drew out his knife all in his right hand.

9. He stabbed her in the heart and the blood it did flow;
   He stabbed her in the heart and the blood it did flow,
   And into the grave pretty Polly did go.

10. He put on a little dirt and he started for home;
    Throwed on a little dirt and he started for home,
    Leaving no one behind but the wild birds to moan.

11. A debt to the devil Willie must pay;
    A debt to the devil Willie must pay;
    For killing pretty Polly and running away.

67.

# ROBIN

*One of the most popular song versions on the taming-of-the-shrew theme.*

Happy, in 2

1. Rob-in, he mar-ried a wife from the West,
2. When she got up, she got up in haste,
3. When she churned she churned in a boot,

mop - i - ty, mop - i - ty, mo, no; ___

1.
2.
3. in -

she turned out to be none of the best.
went to the cup-board be - fore she was laced  } with a
stead of a cra - dle she put in her foot.

68.

high - jig - jig - i - ty    top    and    pet - ti - coat,

Rob-in  a  thrush cried  mo - no - no. _____

4. She made her cheese upon the shelf,
   When it turned, it turned of itself.

5. The cheese fell out upon the floor,
   Jumped up on its feet and ran out of the door.

6. It ran 'til it came to Wakefield Cross,
   She followed after upon a white horse.

7. This song was made for gentlemen,
   If you want any more, I will sing it again.

le Goullon

69.

# WHY, SOLDIERS, WHY?

Forcefully, in 4

1. How stands the glass a - round? For shame, ye take no
2. Why, __ sol - diers, why should we be mel - an -
3. 'Tis __ but __ vain, ( I mean not to up -

care, my boys; how stands the glass a - round? Let
chol - y, boys? Why, __ sol - diers, why? Whose
braid you, boys ), 'tis __ but __ vain for

mirth and wine __ a - bound. The trum - pets __
bus - 'ness 'tis __ to __ die. What? sigh - ing?
sol - diers to __ com - plain; should next cam -

Gossip says General Wolfe sang this song the night before
his victory and death at Quebec in 1759. The song became known throughout the colonies as "Wolfe's Song."

sound!     The col - ors fly - ing_ are, my boys, to
Fie!       Drink on, drown fear, be_ jol - ly, boys; 'tis
paign      send us  to Him that made you, boys, we're

fight, kill, or wound, con - tent    with    our hard fare,   my
he,   you or I; cold,   hot,    wet,    or   dry,_    we're
free  from    pain; but should    we    re - main,_   a

boys, _____ on _____ the    cold _    ground.
al - ways bound to   fol - low, boys, and   scorn to   fly.
bot - tle and a kind  land - la - dy cures   all   a -  gain.

71.

# ON SPRINGFIELD MOUNTAIN

*Unique among folk songs this song was originally written in 1761 as an elegy to the tune of "Old Hundred." It tells of the sad death of Timothy Myrick, twenty-two and engaged to marry, who was bitten by a rattlesnake in Farmington, Massachusetts. The melody we find here was written in 1840, when the song was performed on the stage as a comic song, "The Pesky Sarpint, a pathetic ballad."*

Slow

On Spring-field Moun-tain there did dwell a love-ly youth, I knowed him well. Ray goo too

CHORUS

day - noo - ay, ray too di - noo - ay, too di
nay hoo - i too di noo.

2. He scarce had mowed half round the field
   When an ug-lye serpent bit his heel.

   *Chorus:*

3. They took him home to Mol-lye dear
   Which made her feel so ve-rye queer.

   *Chorus:*

4. Now Mol-lye had two ruby lips
   With which the pizen she did sip.

   *Chorus:*

5. Now Mol-lye had a rotten tooth
   And so the pizen killed them both.

# THE BOLD SOLDIER

*During the colonial period, the English were fighting on land and sea against Portuguese, French, and Spanish. Professional soldiers going to or coming from the wars were known everywhere in England. Captain Miles Standish and Captain John Smith were typical English soldiers of fortune.*

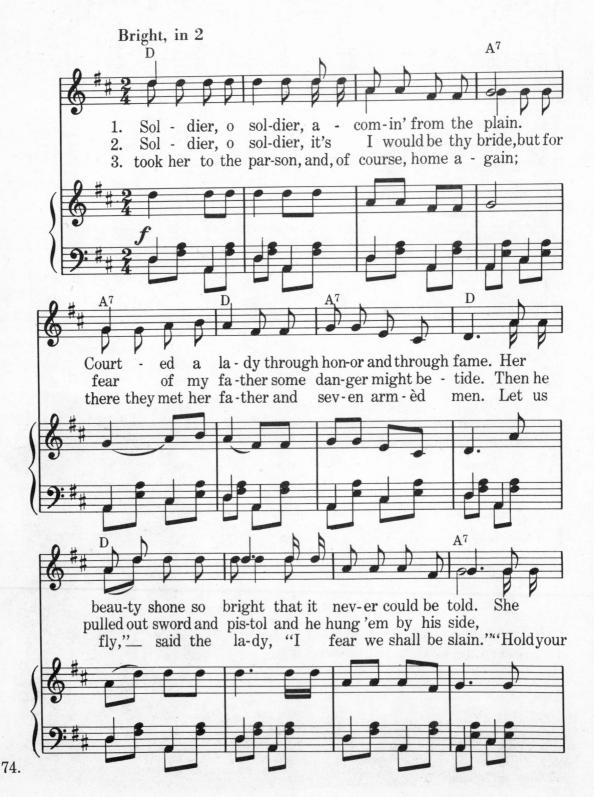

Bright, in 2

1. Sol - dier, o sol-dier, a - com-in' from the plain.
2. Sol - dier, o sol-dier, it's I would be thy bride, but for
3. took her to the par-son, and, of course, home a - gain;

Court - ed a la - dy through hon-or and through fame. Her
fear of my fa-ther some dan-ger might be - tide. Then he
there they met her fa-ther and sev-en arm-èd men. Let us

beau-ty shone so bright that it nev-er could be told. She
pulled out sword and pis-tol and he hung 'em by his side,
fly,"— said the la-dy, "I fear we shall be slain.""Hold your

al-ways loved the sol- dier be-cause he was so bold.
swore he would be mar-ried, no mat-ter what be-tide. Fa-la-
hand, said the sol-dier, "Nev-er fear a-gain."

CHORUS:

la-la, _____ Fa-la - la - la-la, _____ Fa-la-

la - la, _____ Fa-la - la - la. _____
2. _____
3. Then he

4. Then he pulléd out sword and pistol and he causéd them to rattle;
   The lady held the horse while the soldier fought in battle.
   "Hold your hand," said the old man, "do not be so bold;
   You shall have my daughter and a thousand pounds of gold."
   Fa-la, etc.

5. "Fight on!" said the lady, "the portion is too small."
   "Hold your hand," said the old man, "you can have it all."
   Then he took them right straight home and he called them son and dear,
   Not because he loved them but only through fear.
   Fa-la, etc.

# YANKEE DOODLE

★ ★ ★ ★ ★ ★ ★ ★ ★ ★ ★ ★ ★ ★ ★

*In the summer or early fall of 1758, during the French and Indian War, a British army surgeon, Dr. Richard Schuckburgh, who had spent most of his life in America, was encamped with General Abercrombie on the old Van Rensselaer estate, near Albany. A number of provincial troops were mobilizing there. Their rustic appearance was so ludicrous that Dr. Schuckburgh, who was quite a wit, wrote a song referring to the colonials as "Yankee Doodles."*

★ ★ ★ ★ ★ ★ ★ ★ ★ ★ ★ ★ ★ ★ ★

Comfortable, in 2

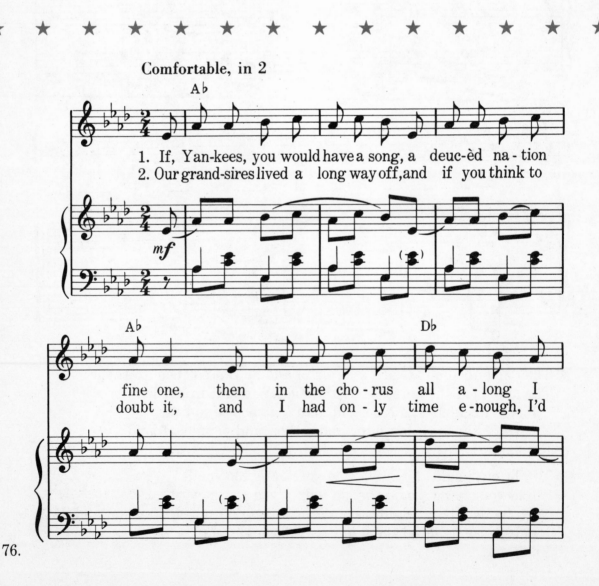

1. If, Yan-kees, you would have a song, a deuc-èd na-tion fine one, then in the cho-rus all a-long I
2. Our grand-sires lived a long way off, and if you think to doubt it, and I had on-ly time e-nough, I'd

guess you'd like to join one. Then Yan - kee Doo - dle,
tell you all a - bout it. Then Yan - kee Doo - dle,

one and all pass 'round the cho - rus hand - y, for
roar a - way and keep the cho - rus hand - y, for

some can sing, and all can bawl Yan-kee Doo-dle Dan-dy.____
some can sing, and all can say_ Yan-kee Doo-dle Dan-dy.____

3. I'd tell you all, how hard they were
For tithes and taxes hinted,
And how they didn't think 'twas fair
And how they got affronted.

*Chorus:*

But Yankee Doodle, all once more,
Keep up the chorus handy,
For some can sing, and all can roar,
Yankee Doodle Dandy.

4. And now of what might them befall
They nothing were afraid in,
So took their wives and children all
And off they push'd for Leyden.

*Chorus:*

Then Yankee Doodle, one and all,
Struck up the chorus handy,
As loud as they could sing and bawl
Yankee Doodle Dandy.

5. And there they got a monstrous ship
As big as any gunboat
And all to fit her for a trip
I guess was nicely done to't.

*Chorus:*

Then Yankee Doodle all aboard!
Pip'd out the boatswain handy
And young and old struck up and
    roar'd
Yankee Doodle Dandy.

6. Then ev'ry man, he seiz'd a rope
And pull'd with all his soul, sir,
And haul'd the tow-cloth all way up
And ti'd it to the pole, sir.

*Chorus:*

Then Yankee Doodle now they go
All in their ship so handy,
And sing All-Saints, Old Hundred too,
And Yankee Doodle Dandy.

7. But when they got away from shore
And 'fore the wind did streak it,
And heard the ocean billows roar
I guess they didn't like it.

*Chorus:*

But Yankee Doodle, never mind,
Strike up the chorus handy,
They'd left th' oppressors far behind
So Yankee Doodle Dandy.

8. And there they saw a great big fish
That thrash'd about his tail, sir
And look so deuced saucyish,
I guess it was a whale, sir.

*Chorus:*

But Yankee Doodle let him go
All in the deep so handy,
While we above and he below
Sing Yankee Doodle Dandy.

9. But now a dreadful storm arose
And dang'rous case they stood in,
And hail, and rain, and sleet, and
    snows,
Fell thick as hasty puddin'.

*Chorus:*

But foul or fair, we're stout and
    strong
In ev'ry lot we're handy;
Then join the chorus, and the song,
Of Yankee Doodle Dandy.

10. The billows they roll'd up on high
Enough the ship to fill, sir,
And toss'd the vessel at the sky
As high as 'chusett hill, sir.

78.

*Chorus:*
But Yankee Doodle, that's the thing
At which we're always handy,
For, high or low, we'll always sing
Yankee Doodle Dandy.

11. And now this noble ship, once more
As staunch as ever man trod,
Approach'd the sandy, desert shore,
And landed them on Cape Cod.

*Chorus:*
Then Yankee Doodle, all again
Join'd in the chorus handy,
And sung aloud with might and main
Yankee Doodle Dandy.

12. When all were safely landed so
Our grand-daddies and grand-dams,
And Sall, and Sue, and Bill, and Joe,
All had a feast on sand-clams!

*Chorus:*
Then Yankee Doodle, all, you know
Join'd in the chorus handy,
And Sall, and Sue, and Bill, and Joe
Sung Yankee Doodle Dandy.

13. To keep the bears and panthers out,
And not less savage wild-man,
Of white pine logs each built a hut,
As big as Father's hog-pen!

*Chorus:*
Then Yankee Doodle let them come,
They'll always find us handy,
With musket balls instead of rum,
So Yankee Doodle Dandy.

14. They planted fields enclos'd with
    stakes
And work'd like dogs or asses,
Made pumpkin pies and Indian cakes
And ate them up with 'lasses.

*Chorus:*
Then Yankee Doodle, one and all
Join'd in the chorus handy,
As loud as they could sing and bawl
Yankee Doodle Dandy.

15. And ev'ry day for many weeks,
Beginning on each Monday,
They watch'd and work'd and fought
    like Greeks,
And went to church on Sunday.

*Chorus:*
For Yankee Doodle, heroes great
In all good works are handy,
In peace, or war, in church, or state,
They're Yankee Doodle Dandy.

Then Yankee Doodle, all once more
Join in the chorus handy,
As loud as you can sing and roar
Yankee Doodle Dandy.

# REVOLUTIONARY AMERICA
## 1775-1790

"History is what happened and folklore is what people think happened," as Frank Shay put it. Songs about historical events are this kind of history. The advantage these songs have over the carefully selected historical note is an emotional vitality about the event in question. If in singing these songs we find ourselves stirred by this emotion we get a sense of the living history that is a part of our country's heritage.

Songs of the American Revolution meant something in our country's development and mean something today. These songs are interesting, playable and singable. They are important not only for content, but for the spirit that caused them to be written.

The emotional upsurge of the Revolutionary War, the heroes of this time of crisis, the arguments that were heatedly presented on both sides, found expression in song. Some songs have their melodic origin in well-known British tunes of the day, others stem directly from the tradition of New England hymn singing. The songs were learned by word of mouth but they were often printed in the newspapers and broadsides of the day.

Songs were used as a means of bringing others to the Revolutionary cause and of keeping morale high. Barlow, the Hartford poet, entering the Revolutionary Army as Chaplain, wrote: "I do not know whether I shall do more for the cause in the capacity of Chaplain, than I would in that of Poet; I have great faith in the influence of songs; and I shall continue, while fulfilling the duties of my appointment, to write one now and then, and to encourage the taste for them which I find in the camp."

**The Eve of the Revolution** — With the first announcement of the Stamp Act in 1765, patriotic lyrics began to appear. Organizations like the Sons of Liberty helped create public demonstrations, terrorized the British collectors, and destroyed their tax stamps. One of the most expressive lyrics of this period is the "Song for the Sons of Liberty," distributed as a broadside and published in many newspapers. The first and last of the six verses read:

> In story we're told how our fathers of old
> Braved the rage of the wind and the waves;
> And cross'd the deep o'er to this desolate shore
> All because they were loath to be slaves, brave boys,
> All because they were loath to be slaves.

81

The birthright we hold shall never be sold
But sacred maintain'd to our graves,
And before we'll comply we'll gallantly die,
For we must not, we will not be slaves, brave boys!
For we must not, we will not be slaves.

The Stamp Act was repealed in 1766, but the next year saw duties on glass, lead, painter's colors, paper, and tea. Tension grew rapidly. In Boston a brawl developed between an unruly street crowd and British troops, and four Bostonians were killed. Strong feelings magnified this incident (the famous Boston Massacre), with broadsides like the following fanning the flames.

Unhappy Boston sees their sons deplore
Thy hallowed walks were smeared with guiltless gore,
While faith was pressed, a mighty savage band
With murderous rank has stretched their bloody hand.

No scalding tears from rage and anguish wrung,
No speechless sorrow seeking for a tongue
For me now weeping world can altered be
The flame did glow for victims such as these.

Meanwhile the loyal British troops stationed in the colonies, who regarded the Americans as rebels, sang their own songs as "On the Banks of the Dee," which tells of a soldier who joined the British forces in America "to quell the Proud Rebels." They also sang "Heart of Oak," "Down Derry Down" and "How Happy the Soldier," some of which the colonists set to words of their own, expressing opposite sentiments. To "Heart of Oak," for example, the Bostonians sang this parody, one of many ridiculing the unpopular British stationed in their city:

'Twas winter and blue Tory noses were freezing
As they marched o'er the land where they ought not to be:
   The Valiants complain'd at the Fifers' curs'd wheezing,
And wish'd they'd remain'd on the banks of the Dee.

Lead on, thou paid Captain! Tramp on, thou proud minions!
Thy ranks, base men, shall be strung like ripe onions,
For here thou hast found heads with warlike opinions,
On shoulders of nobles who ne'er saw the Dee.

The New England hymns themselves took on a secular and patriotic tone, and popular hymns often had an anti-British slant. The leader of this hymn development was William Billings of Boston (1746-1800), a self-taught musician who started life as a tanner. He founded singing societies and reformed church music and church choirs, introducing the pitch pipe and instruments to accompany the voices. As controversy mounted and meetings were forbidden, such singing societies served both as a place where patriotic hymns could be learned and where current events were discussed and action was quietly organized.

In 1770 the first of Billings' books of hymns appeared, engraved by Paul Revere. Its title page read:

The New England Psalm-Singer, or American Chorister.
Containing a Number of Psalm-Tunes, Anthems and Canons
In Four and Five Parts. (Never before published.)
Composed by William Billings, A Native of Boston,
In New England.

Math. XXI, 16, "Out of the Mouth of Babes and Sucklings
            hast Thou perfected Praise."
James V, 13   "Is any merry? Let him sing Psalms."
            "O, praise the Lord with one consent,
            And, in this grand design,
            Let Britain and the Colonies
            Unanimously join."
Boston, New England, Printed by Edes and Gill.

Billings' patriotic hymns appeared in this and five subsequent volumes.

The poet, the satirist, and the writer of songs were so highly regarded as supplying weapons to fight the Revolutionary War that most of the wits of the day employed their leisure in writing patriotic songs. There was a great deal of controversial writing in the newspapers, and a great increase in the number of satiric, dramatic, poetic broadsides.

One of the first of such writers was Dr. Joseph Warren of Boston who wrote "Free America" in 1774 to the tune of "The British Grenadier." Another great writer of the time, many of whose poems were sung, was Philip Freneau. One of his war songs written in 1776, began:

> Hark, Hark, the sound of war is heard,
>     And we must all attend;
> Take up our arms and go with speed
>     Our country to defend.
>
> Our parent state has turned our foe,
>     Which fills our land with pain;
> Her gallant ships manned out for war
>     Come thundering o'er the main.

The Revolutionary War—The War began with "Yankee Doodle," for it was to this melody the British troops marched out of Boston to the relief of their comrades at Lexington one April night in 1775. Indeed, most of the battles of the Revolution were described in verse, and a great many of the verses were set to music. Typical of the wit that went into these verse descriptions are these verses sung by the Minute Men who penned the British troops up in Boston and cut off their food supply:

> How brave ye went out
>     With your muskets all bright,
> And thought to be-frighten
>     The folds with the sight;
> But when you got there
>     How they ponder'd your puns,
> And all the way home
>     How they pepper'd your bums,
> And is it not, honies, a comical crack,
> To be proud in the face, and be shot in the back?

And what have you got now
  With all your designing,
But a town without victuals
  To sit down and dine in,
And to look on the ground
  Like a parcel of noodles,
And sing, how the Yankees
  Have beaten the doodles?
I'm sure if you're wise
  You'll make peace for a dinner,
For fighting and fasting
  Will soon make ye thinner.

We seldom hear of the Tories who set themselves up against the course of the Revolution, but about one-third of the colonists were loyalists. There were many Tory newspapers, Tory broadsides, and Tory songs. The British had their songs from overseas and made up many on their current fight. One amusing one from the New York *Gazette* ridicules their own General Howe, whose popularity was small and whose fondness for women was famous.

Awake! Awake! Sir Billy,
There's forage in the plain.
Ah! Leave your little filly
And open the campaign.

Heed not a woman's prattle
Which tickles in the ear
But give the word for battle
And grasp the warlike spear.

Another extols the British Light Infantry, stationed at New York, which was making sporadic raids on Washington's stores:

For battle prepared in their country's just cause
Their King to avenge and support all his laws;
As fierce as a tiger, as swift as the roe,
The British Light Infantry rush on their foe.

The War ended as it had begun, to the tune of "Yankee Doodle," but this time it was the American Army who played the melody.

At the surrender in 1781, General Cornwallis, pleading illness, did not appear. His substitute, General O'Hara, prepared to give up his sword to General Washington, but was referred to General Lincoln, who received the sword and at once handed it back. As the British soldiers laid down their arms their band played a quaint old English melody entitled, appropriately, "The World Turned Upside Down." With equal suitability the Continental Army's band played "Yankee Doodle."

Washington's statement to his troops before the surrender was a beautiful conclusion: "My brave fellows, let no shouting, no clamorous huzzahing increase their mortification. It is sufficient to us that we witness their humiliation. Posterity will huzzah for us."

**LIBERTY**

# WHAT A COURT HATH OLD ENGLAND

*Despite the support of Pitt, Burke, and other Englishmen who opposed the Stamp Act, tension heightened between the colonies and England. This satire, sung to the tune of "Down Derry Down," follows the pattern of "Liberty Hall," written by George Stevens of London in 1757. As the song indicates, the colonists were ready to take up arms.*

Like a chant

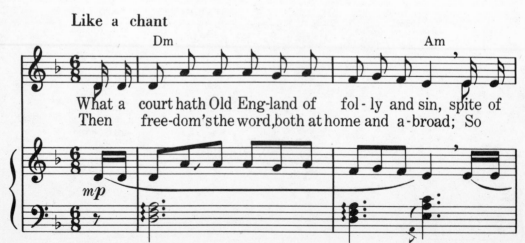

What a court hath Old Eng-land of fol-ly and sin, spite of
Then free-dom's the word, both at home and a-broad; So

Chat-ham and Cam-den, Bar-re, Burke, Wilkes and Glynn! Not con-
out with each scab-bard that hides a good sword! Our

tent with the game act, they taxed fish and sea, and A-
fore-fa-thers gave us this free-dom in hand, and we'll

mer-i-ca drench with hot wa-ter and tea. Der-ry
die in de-fence of the rights of the land. Der-ry

down, down,_____ down der-ry down._____

# HEART OF OAK

*Many songs have been written to the original "Heart of Oak" presented here. First sung in London in 1759, the words are by the famous actor David Garrick, the melody by Dr. Boyce.*

With dignity

1. Come, cheer up, my lads, 'tis to glo-ry we steer, to
2. Our wor-thy fore-fath-ers, let's give them a cheer, to

add some-thing more to this won-der-ful year; to
cli-mates un-known did cou-ra-geous-ly steer: through

hon - or we call you, as free men, not slaves, for
o - ceans, to des - erts, for free - dom they came, and

88.

who are so free as the sons of the waves? Heart of
dy - ing be-queath'd us their free - dom and fame.

CHORUS:

oak are our ships, heart of oak are our men; we

al - ways are read - y, stead - y, boys, stead - y, we'll

fight __ and we'll con - quer a - gain and a - gain.

89.

# THE LIBERTY SONG

*In 1768, John Dickinson of Delaware, later a member of the first Congress, wrote "The Liberty Song," to the tune of "Heart of Oak." Like other songs of its kind, it became widely known, being printed as a broadside and in newspapers.*

★ ★ ★ ★ ★ ★ ★ ★ ★ ★ ★ ★ ★ ★ ★ ★ ★ ★ ★ ★ ★

1. Come join hand in hand, brave Americans all,
And rouse your bold hearts at fair liberty's call;
No tyrannous acts shall suppress your just claim,
Or stain with dishonor America's name.

*Chorus:* In freedom we're born and in freedom we'll live
Our purses are ready
Steady, friends, steady,
Not as slaves but as free men our money we'll give.

2. Our worthy forefathers—let's give them a cheer—
To climates unknown did courageously steer:
Through oceans, to deserts, for freedom they came,
And dying bequeath'd us their freedom and fame.

*Chorus*

3. The tree their own hands had to liberty rear'd;
They lived to behold growing strong and rever'd;
With transport they cry'd, "Now our witness we gain
For our children shall gather the fruits of our pain."

*Chorus*

4. All ages shall speak with amaze and applause,
Of the courage we'll show in support of our laws;
To die we can bear, but serve we disdain,
For shame is to freedom more dreadful than pain.

*Chorus*

★ ★ ★ ★ ★ ★ ★ ★ ★ ★ ★ ★ ★ ★ ★ ★ ★ ★ ★ ★ ★

*Rallying songs were on everyone's lips; even the children were included. A broadside sheet of 1775, afterwards reprinted in The Constitutional Gazette of New York, suggested that parents teach the alphabet to their children as follows:*

# ALPHABET FOR LITTLE MASTERS AND MISSES

A stands for Americans who scorn to be slaves;

B for Boston, where fortitude their freedom saves;

C for Congress, which, though loyal, will be free;

D stands for defence, 'gainst force and tyranny.

*Chorus:* Stand firmly, A and Z, We swear for ever to be free!

E stands for evils, which a civil war must bring;

F stands for fate, dreadful to both people and king;

G stands for George, may God give him wisdom and grace;

H stands for hypocrite, who wears a double face.

*Chorus*

J stands for justice which traitors in power defy,

K stands for King, who should to such the axe apply;

L stands for London, to its country ever true,

M stands for Mansfield, who hath another view.

*Chorus*

N stands for North, who to the House the Mandate brings,

O stands for oaths, binding on subjects not on kings:

P stands for people, who their freedom should defend,

Q stands for quere, when will England's troubles end?

*Chorus*

R stands for rebels, not at Boston but at home,

S stands for Stuart, sent by Whigs abroad to roam

T stands for Tories, who may try to bring them back,

V stands for villains, who have well deserved the rack.

*Chorus*

W stands for Wilkes, who us from warrants saved,

Y for York, the New, half corrupted, half enslaved,

Z stands for Zero, but means the Tory minions,

Who threaten us with fire and sword, to bias our opinions.

*Chorus:* Stand firmly, A and Z, We swear for ever to be free!

# THE BALLAD of the TEA PARTY

*The words of this and the following song, both about the
Boston Tea Party, were written long after the event. The
melody, first heard in 1730, is from an old sea song,"Come
and Listen to My Ditty," or "The Sailor's Complaint."*

**Steady, in 2**

1. Tea-ships near to Bos-ton ly - ing, on the wharf a
2. Armed with ham-mers, ax - es, chi-sels, wea-pons new for

num-er-ous crew. Sons of free-dom, nev - er dy - ing,
war - like deed, toward the tax - èd, freight-ed ves - sels

92.

3. Overboard she goes, my boys, heave—
Ho where darling waters roar:
We love our cup of tea full well but
Love our freedom more.

*Chorus:* With a rinktum, dinktum,
fa la linktum,
Love our freedom more.

4. Deep, into the sea descended
Curséd weed of China's coast;
Thus at once our fears were ended,
Rights shall ne'er be lost!

*Chorus:* With a rinktum, dinktum,
fa la linktum,
Rights shall ne'er be lost!

# THE BOSTON TEA TAX

Steady, in 2

1. I snum I am a Yan-kee lad, and I
2. And t'oth-er day the Yan-kee folks were ___
3. And then a-board the ships we went our ___

guess I'll sing a dit-ty; ___ and ___ if you do not
mad a-bout the tax-es, ___ and ___ so we went like
ven-geance to ad-min-is-ter, we ___ did-n't care one

rel-ish it, the more 'twill be the pit-y; ___ that
In-juns dress'd to split tea chests with ax-es. ___ It
tar-nal bit for an-y king or min-is-ter. We

is, I think I should have been a plague-y sight more
was the year of sev'n-ty-three and we felt real-ly
made a plague-y mess of tea in one of the big-gest

fin-ished man. If \_ I'd been born in Bos-ton town, but I
grit-ty.\_ The \_ May-or would have led the gang, but \_
dish-es; \_ I \_ mean we steeped it in the sea and \_

warn't 'cause I'm a coun-try man.
Bos-ton warn't a ci-ty! Fol-de-rol-de-ray, Fol-de-
treat-ed all the fish-es.

but I warn't 'cause I'm a coun-try man.
rol-de-ray, but \_ Bos-ton warn't a ci-ty!
and \_ treat-ed all the fish-es.

# FREE AMERICA

*The writer of this song was Dr. Joseph Warren of Boston, one of the original Minute Men. It was he who started Paul Revere off on his famous ride in 1775. He was killed in the first major engagement of the war, Bunker Hill. He used the well-known melody of "The British Grenadier."*

Martial (heavy accents on every beat)

1. Born from a world of ty - rants, be - neath the west-ern sky we'll form a new do - min - ion, a __

2. Lift up your heads, ye he - roes, and swear with proud dis - dain: that wretch that would en - snare you, shall

96.

3. Lift up your heads, ye heroes, and swear with proud disdain
   That wretch that would ensnare you, shall lay his snares in vain.
   Should Europe empty all her force,
   We'll meet her in array . . .
   And fight and shout, and shout and fight
   For North Americay.

# CHESTER

*New England congregations were social as well as religious centers. They sang secular hymns and, as tension grew with England, patriotic ones too. "Chester," from William Billings' collection, The Singing Master's Assistant, 1778, was sung as a marching song from Maine to Georgia.*

Like a march (not too slow)

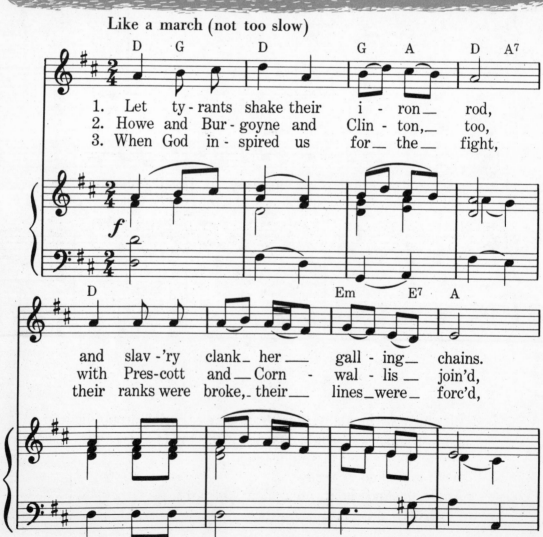

1. Let ty-rants shake their i - ron rod,
2. Howe and Bur-goyne and Clin - ton, too,
3. When God in-spired us for the fight,

and slav-'ry clank her gall - ing chains.
with Pres-cott and Corn - wal - lis join'd,
their ranks were broke, their lines were forc'd,

We'll fear them not; we trust in God:
New England's God forever reigns.

to-geth-er plot our o-ver-throw,
in one infer-nal league combin'd.

their ships were shelter'd in our sight,
or swiftly driven from our coast.

4. The foe comes on with haughty stride,
   Our troops advance with martial noise,
   Their vet'rans flee before our youth,
   And generals yield to beardless boys.

5. What grateful offering shall we bring,
   What shall we render to the Lord?
   Loud hallelujahs let us sing,
     And praise His name on every chord.

99.

# YANKEE DOODLE (1775)

★ ★ ★ ★ ★ ★ ★ ★ ★ ★ ★ ★ ★ ★ ★ ★ ★ ★ ★

1. Father and I went down to camp,
Along with Captain Good'n,
And there we saw the men and boys
As thick as hasty puddin.

*Chorus:*

Yankee Doodle keep it up,
Yankee Doodle Dandy,
Mind the music and the step,
And with the girls be handy.

2. There was Captain Washington
Upon a slapping stallion,
Giving orders to his men—
I guess there was a million.

*Chorus*

3. And then the feathers on his hat,
They look'd so tarnal fina,
I wanted peskily to get
To give to my Jemina.

*Chorus*

4. And there they had a swampin' gun
As large as log of maple,
On a deucéd little cart—
A load for Father's cattle;

*Chorus*

5. And every time they fired it off,
It took a horn of powder;
It made a noise like Father's gun,
Only a nation louder.

*Chorus*

6. And Captain Davis had a gun,
He kind-a clapt his hand on't,
And stuck a crooked stabbing iron
Upon the little end on't.

*Chorus*

7. And there I see a pumpkin shell,
As big as Mother's basin,
And every time they touch'd it off,
They scamper'd like the nation.

*Chorus*

8. And there I see a little keg,
Its heads were made of leather—
They knock'd upon't with little sticks
To call the folks together.

*Chorus*

9. And there they fife away like fun,
And play on cornstock fiddles,
And some had ribands red as blood,
All wound about their middles.

*Chorus*

10. The troopers, too, would gallop up
And fire right in our faces;
It scar'd me almost half to death
To see them run such races.

*Chorus*

11. I see another snarl of men
A-digging graves, they told me,
So tarnal long, so tarnal deep,
They tencéd they should hold me.

*Chorus*

12. But I can't tell you half I see
They kept up such a smother;
So I took my hat off—made a bow,
And scamper'd home to Mother.

*Chorus*

100.

The well-known "Yankee Doodle" melody served for many Revolutionary war incidents in verse. This version, said to have been composed in 1775 when Washington assumed command of the Continental Army, mentions many kinds of firearms used by the colonials. The Continental Army was little organized as to army discipline, but its individuals were excellent marksmen. They had constant practice against the Indians and long experience in the French and Indian War.

Washington himself had trained in the Virginia Militia and with one-fifth of all the able-bodied colonials had fought in the French and Indian War. According to Thomas Jefferson, Washington was the greatest horseman of his time. When he left Virginia to assume command of the Continental Army, then besieging the British in Boston, he brought with him five horses of his own breeding. One of these is probably the "slapping stallion" of the second verse.

# THE RIFLEMEN'S SONG AT BENNINGTON

General Burgoyne's disasters, en route from Canada to Albany by way of Lake Champlain, were recorded in popular contemporary ballads. At Bennington one of his foraging detachments was surrounded, killed, or captured by 800 ill-armed villagers who rallied in a driving rain.

# THE RIFLEMEN'S SONG AT BENNINGTON

Like a March

1. Why come ye hith-er, Red-coats, your mind what mad-ness
2. Ye ride a good-ly steed, ye may know an-oth-er
3. Tell he who stays at home, or cross the brin-y

fills? In our val-leys there is dan-ger, and there's
mas-ter. Ye for-ward came with speed, but you'll
wa-ters, that thith-er ye must come, like

dan-ger on our hills. Oh, hear ye not the
learn to back much fas-ter. Then you'll meet our Moun-tain
bul-locks to the slaugh-ter. If we the work must

102.

103.

# THE BATTLE OF SARATOGA

**Steady, in 2**

1. Come un-to me, ye he-roes, and I the truth will tell__ con-
2. Be-fore the Ti-con-der-o-ga, full well both night and day__ their

cern-ing man-y a sol-dier who for his coun-try fell.__ Bur-
mo-tions we ob-served__ be-fore the blood-y fray;__ Bur-

goyne, the King's com-mand-er and curs-èd To-ry crew,__ with
goyne sent Baum to Benn-ing-ton, with Hes-sians there he went,__ to

CHORUS:

105.

# THE BATTLE OF SARATOGA

3. But little did they know then
    with whom they had to deal.
It was not quite so easy
    our stores and stocks to steal.
Stark would give them only
    a portion of his lead,
With half his crew ere sunset,
    Baum lay among the dead.

4. The 19th of September,
    the morning cool and clear,
Gates addressed the army
    each soldier's heart to cheer.
"Burgoyne," he cried, "advances,
    but we will never fly,
But rather than surrender,
    we'll fight him till we die!"

5. The Seventh of October,
    they did capitulate,
Burgoyne and his proud army
    we did our prisoners make.
And vain was their endeavor
    our men to terrify,
Though death was all around us,
    not one of us would fly!

6. Now here's a health to Herkimer
    and our commander Gates!
To Freedom and to Washington
    whom every Tory hates.
Likewise unto our Congress—
    God grant it long to reign—
Our country, rights and justice
    forever to maintain!

*Almost every major battle of the Revolution was cele-
brated in verse. The following rhyming summary of
the Batte of Saratoga is from a newspaper account:*

Here followeth the direful fate
Of Burgoyne and his army great
Who so proudly did display
The terrors of despotic sway
His power and pride and many threats
Have been brought low by fort'nate Gates
To bend to the United States

British prisoners by Convention . . . . . . . . . . . . . . . . . . 2442
Foreigners—by Contra-vention . . . . . . . . . . . . . . . . 2198
Tories sent across the Lake . . . . . . . . . . . . . . . . . . 1100
Burgoyne and his suite, in state . . . . . . . . . . . . . . . . 12
Sick and wounded, bruised and pounded ⎱
Ne'er so much before confounded ⎰ . . . . . . . . . . 528
Prisoners of war before Convention . . . . . . . . . . . 400
Deserters come with kind intention . . . . . . . . . . . 300
They lost at Bennington's great battle ⎱
Where Stark's glorious arms did rattle ⎰ . . . . . . 1220
Kill'd in September and October . . . . . . . . . . . . 600
Ta'en by brave Brown, some drunk, some sober . . . . . . . . 413
Slain by high-famed Herkerman . . . . . . . . . . . . 300
On both flanks, on rear and van ⎫
Indians, suttlers, butchers, drovers, ⎪
Enough to crowd large plains all over ⎪
And those whom grim Death did prevent ⎪
From fighting against our continent; ⎬
And also those who stole away, ⎪ . . . . . . . . . . . 4413
Lest they down their arms should lay, ⎪
Abhorring that obnoxious day; ⎪
The whole make fourteen thousand men ⎪
Who may not with us fight again ⎭

                                                    ―――――――
                                                    14,000

This is a pretty just account
Of Burgoyne's legion's whole amount,
Who came across the Northern Lakes
To desolate our happy States.
Their brass cannons we have got all
Fifty-six both great and small;
And ten thousand stand of arms,
To prevent all future harms.
Among our prisoners there are
Six generals, of fame most rare;
Six members of their Parliament—
Reluctantly they seem content;
Three British lords and Lord Belcarras,
Who came, our country free to harass.
Two baronets, of high extraction,
Were sorely wounded in the action

107.

# THE YANKEE MAN-OF-WAR

*The brilliant exploits of John Paul Jones cheered the morale*
*of the rebelling colonists and gave rise to ballads like this.*

Like a march

1. 'Tis of a gal-lant Yan-kee ship that flew the stripes and
2. It was a clear and cloud-less night, and the wind blew stead-y and
3. There was no talk of short-'ning sail by him who walked the

stars,— and the whis-tling wind from the west nor'-west blew
strong,— as— fair-ly o-ver the spark-ling deep our
poop,— and— under the press of her pon-d'ring jib the

through the pitch-pine spars,— with her star-board tacks— a-
good ship bowled a-long;— with the foam-ing seas— be-
boom bent like a hoop!— and the groan-ing wa-ter-ways

board, my boys, she hung up - on the gale; __ on an
neath her bow the fier - y waves she spread, __ and __
told the strain that held her stout main tack, __ but he

au - tumn night we raised the light on the old head of Kin - sale.
bend - ing low her bos - om of snow, she bur - ied her lee, cat-head.
on - ly laughed as he glanced a loft at a white and sil - v'ry track.

4. The nightly robes our good ship wore were her own topsails three,
Her spanker and her standing jib, the courses being free;
Now lay aloft! my heroes bold, let not a moment pass!
And royals and topgallant sails were quickly on each mast.

5. What looms upon our starboard bow? What hangs upon the breeze?
'Tis time our good ship hauled her wind abreast the old saltee's.
For by her ponderous press of sail and by her escorts four,
We saw our morning visitor was a British man-of-war.

6. Up spoke our noble captain then, and a shot ahead of us passed,
"Haul snug your flowing courses! Lay your topsail to the mast!"
Those Englishmen gave three loud hurrahs from the deck of their covered ark
And we answered back by a solid broadside from the deck of our patriot bark.

7. "Out booms! Out booms!" our skipper cried, "Out booms
        and give her sheet,"
And the swiftest keel that ever was launched shot ahead of the British fleet,
And amidst a thundering shower of shot with the stun-sails hoisting away,
Down the north channel Paul Jones did steer just at the break of day.

# JOHNNY HAS GONE FOR A SOLDIER

*An anonymous American song popular with the colonials.*

**Slowly, free in delivery**

1. — Here I sit on But-ter-milk Hill, who could blame me
2. I'd sell my clock, I'd sell my reel, like-wise I'd sell my

cry my fill? And ev-'ry tear would turn a mill;
spin-ning wheel to buy my love a sword of steel;

**CHORUS:**

John-ny has gone for a sol-dier. — Shoo-lie, shoo-lie,
John-ny has gone for a sol-dier. —

shoo - lie __ too, shoo - lie, sac - ca - rac - ca bib - ba - lib - ba boo. If I should die for Sal - ly Bo - bo - link come bib - ba - lib - ba boo sa - ro - ra.

111.

# HOW HAPPY THE SOLDIER

*This favorite of the British soldiers during the Revolutionary War was picked up by the Americans; it was sung by both sides in the War of 1812.*

Easy-going, in 2

1. How hap-py the sol-dier who lives on his pay, and
2. He cares not a Mar-ne-dy how the world goes; his

spends half a crown on six-pence a day; he
King finds his quar-ters, and mon-ey and clothes; he

fears nei-ther jus-tic-es, war-rants, nor bums, but
laughs at all sor-row when-ev-er it comes, and

112.

pays all his debts with a roll of his drums, with a
ratt-les a-way with the roll of his drums, with a

row de dow, row de dow, row de dow, dow, and he

pays all his debts with a roll of his drums.

3. The drum is his glory, his joy, and delight,
   It leads him to pleasure as well as to fight;
   No girl, when she hears it, though ever so glum,
   But packs up her tatters, and follows the drum.
   With row de dow, row de dow, row de dow, dow;
   And he pays all his debts with the roll of his drums.

# THE BATTLE OF THE KEGS

*The verses are by Francis Hopkinson, who sang them to General Washington to the tune of "Yankee Doodle." Kegs charged with gunpowder were designed to submerge and float down the river toward the British ships. They were to explode on contact.*

★ ★ ★ ★ ★ ★ ★ ★ ★ ★ ★ ★ ★ ★

1. Gallácounts attend and hear a friend
Trill forth harmonious ditty,
Strange things I'll tell which
   late befell
In Philadelphia city.

2. 'Twas early day, as poets say,
Just when the sun was rising,
A soldier stood on a log of wood,
And saw a thing surprising.

3. As in amaze he stood to gaze,
The truth can't be deny'd, sir,
He spy'd a score of kegs or more
Come floating down the tide, sir.

4. A sailor too in jerkin blue,
This strange appearance viewing,
First rubb'd his eyes, in great
   surprise,
Then said, "Some mischief's brewing.

5. "These kegs, I'm told, the rebels
   bold,
Pack'd up like pickling herring;
And they're come down t'attack
   the town,
In this new way of ferrying."

6. The soldier flew, the sailor too,
And scar'd almost to death, sir,
Wore out their shoes, to spread
   the news,
And ran till out of breath, sir.

7. Now up and down throughout
   the town,
Most frantic scenes were acted:
Some ran here, and some ran there,
Like men almost distracted.

8. Some fire cry'd, which some deny'd,
But said the earth had quaked;
And girls and boys, with hideous
   noise,
Ran through the street half naked.

9. Sir William he, snug as a flea,
Lay all this time a-snoring,
Nor dream'd of harm as he lay
   warm,
In bed with Mrs. Loring.

10. Now in a fright, he starts upright,
Awak'd by such a clatter;
He rubs both eyes, and boldly cries,
"For God's sake, what's the matter?"

11. At his bedside he then espy'd
Sir Erskine at command, sir,
Upon one foot, he had one boot,
And th'other in his hand, sir.

12. "Arise, arise," Sir Erskine cries,
"The rebels—more's the pity,
Without a boat, are all afloat
And rang'd before the city."

114.

13. "The motley crew, in vessels new,
With Satan for their guide, sir;
Pack'd up in bags, or wooden kegs,
Come driving down the tide, sir.

14. "Therefore prepare for bloody
war,
These kegs must all be routed,
Or surely we'll despiséd be,
And British courage doubted."

15. The royal band, now ready stand
All rang'd in dread array, sir;
With stomach stout to see it out,
And make a bloody day, sir.

16. The cannons roar from shore to
shore,
The small arms make a rattle;
Since wars began I'm sure no man
E'er saw so strange a battle.

17. The rebel dales, the rebel vales,
With rebel trees surrounded;
The distant woods, the hills and
floods,
With rebel echoes sounded.

18. The fish below swam to and fro,
Attack'd from every quarter;
Why, sure, thought they, the
mischief's to pay
'Mongst folks above the water.

19. The kegs, 'tis said, though
strongly made,
Of rebel staves and hoops, sir;
Could not oppose their pow'rful foes,
The conqu'ring British troops, sir.

20. From morn to night these men of
might
Display'd amazing courage;
And when the sun was fairly down
Return'd to sup their porridge.

21. An hundred men with each a pen,
Or more, upon my word, sir,
It is most true, would be too few,
Their valor to record, sir.

22. Such feats they did perform that
day,
Against those wicked kegs, sir,
That years to come, if they get home,
They'll make their boasts and brags,
sir.

★  ★  ★  ★  ★  ★  ★  ★  ★  ★  ★  ★  ★  ★

*The British discovered the kegs and fired their small arms and cannon
at everything floating in the river at ebbtide. Most of the kegs blew up
among the ice cakes; only one boat was destroyed.*

# Sir Peter Parker

Waltz tempo

1. My Lords, with your leave, an ac-count I will give which de-serves to be writ-ten in me-ter: How the reb-els and I have been pret-ty

2. With la-bor and toil, un-to Sul-li-van's isle I sailed, swift as Fal-staff or Pis-tol, but the Yan-kees, dod rat'em, I could-n't get

3. Dev-il take 'em, their shot came swift and so hot, and the cow-ard-ly dogs stood so stiff, Sir, that I put ship a-bout and was glad to get

Sir Peter Parker, commanding the British man-of-war Bristol, *while attacking Charleston received a heavy cannonading from the rebels.* His breeches were torn off and his thigh wounded.

The Constitutional Gazetteer remarked:
"If 'Honor in the breech is lodged,'
As Hudibras has shown,
It may from thence be fairly judged
Sir Peter's honor's gone."

nigh, faith, al-most too nigh for Sir Pe-ter! __ Ri
at 'em, so ter-rib-ly mauled my poor Bris-tol. __ Ri
out or they would-n't have left me a skiff, Sir. __ Ri

CHORUS

tu-den di-o, ri tu-den di-ay, Faith,
tu-den di-o, ri tu-den di-ay, so
tu-den di-o, ri tu-den di-ay, or they

al-most too nigh for Sir Pe-ter! ____
ter-rib-ly mauled my poor Bris-tol. ____
would-n't have left me a skiff, Sir. ____

117.

4. Now Clinton by land did quietly stand,
   While my guns made a terrible rumpus:
   But my pride took a fall when a well-aiméd ball
   Propelled me along on my bumpus!
   Ri tuden dio, ri tuden diay, propelled me along on my bumpus!

5. Now bold as a Turk, I sailed for New York,
   Where with Clinton and Howe you may find me:
   I'd the wind at my tail and I'm hoisting my sail
   To leave Sullivan's Island behind me.
   Ri tuden dio, ri tuden diay, to leave Sullivan's Island behind me!

*The naval actions of the Revolution received their full share of celebration in verse and song. By the end of 1776 there were 136 privateers at sea with commissions from the Naval Committee of the Continental Congress. John Paul Jones was, of course, the most famous of these with his actions on the* Ranger *and on the famous* Bon Homme Richard, *which sank in the moonlight off the Yorkshire cliffs after a battle with the British* Serapis.

# CORNWALLIS COUNTRY DANCE

*Burgoyne was defeated at Saratoga, Howe was in Philadelphia, and Cornwallis campaigned in Carolina and Virginia. Although he took Charleston and Savannah, the guerrilla warfare of Marion, Sumter, and the Mountain Boys made his campaign ineffective. His retreating and advancing, as he fought General Greene back and forth through North Carolina and Virginia, reminded an unknown balladeer of the "Contre Dance," where two facing lines move back and forth. The English dance tune to which the ballad is set became very popular in the United States in the early 19th Century as "Pop Goes the Weasel."*

119.

# CORNWALLIS COUNTRY DANCE

Comfortable (with a rather steady beat)

1. Corn-wal-lis led a coun-try dance the like was nev-er seen, Sir,— Much ret-ro-grade and much ad-vance, and all with Gen-er-al Green, Sir.— They
2. Quoth he, my guards are wea-ry grown with do-ing coun-try danc-es.— They nev-er at St. James had shown at ca-pers, kicks, or pranc-es.— No
3. Good Wash-ing-ton, Co-lum-bi-a's son, whom ea-sy na-ture taught, Sir,— Now hand in hand they cir-cle round in ev-'ry danc-ing mood, Sir,— The

ram-bled up, they ram-bled down, joined hands,and off they
men so gal - lant there were seen while saun-t'ring on pa-
gen - tle move-ment soon con-founds, the Earl's ___ day draws

run, Sir,— of Gen-er-al Green to Charles-town, the
rade, Sir,— or danc-ing o'er the park so green, or
near, Sir,— the gen - tle move-ment soon con-founds, the

Earl to Wil-ming-ton, Sir. ___
at the mas-quer-ade. Sir. ___
Earl's ___ day draws near, Sir. ___

4. His music soon forgets to play, his feet can't move no more, Sir,
And all his men now curse the day they jigged to our shore, Sir.
Now, Tories all, what can you say . . . Cornwallis is no griper,
But while your hopes are danced away, it's you that pay the piper.

# THE WORLD UPSIDE TURNED DOWN

*At the surrender of Cornwallis at Yorktown which ended the Revolutionary fighting in October, 1781, the colonists played "Yankee Doodle" while the British with equal suitability played a quaint English melody, "The World Turned Upside Down."*

In 2

If but - ter - cups buzz'd af - ter the bee, if

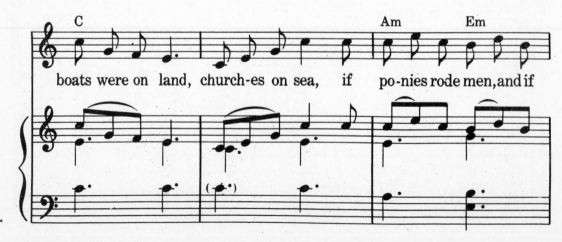

boats were on land, church-es on sea, if po-nies rode men, and if

grass ate the cows, and cats should be chased in-to holes by the mouse,

if the ma-mas sold their ba-bies to the gyp-sies for

half a crown, if sum-mer were spring, and the

oth-er way 'round, then all the world would be up-side down.

123.

# MY DAYS HAVE BEEN SO WONDROUS FREE

*Francis Hopkinson of Philadelphia, (1732-1791), one of our first composers, wrote this song in 1759. Satirist, poet, inventor and painter, Hopkinson became our first Secretary of the Navy.*

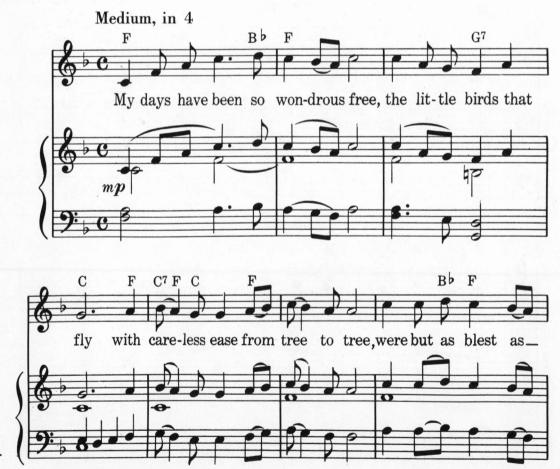

My days have been so won-drous free, the lit-tle birds that

fly with care-less ease from tree to tree, were but as blest as

124.

I, were but as blest as I. Ask the glid-ing wa-ters

if _ a _ tear_ of _ mine in - creased their stream, and

ask the breath -ing gales if ev - er I lent a _ sigh to

them, _ if I lent _ a _ sigh to them.

125.

Francis Hopkinson was an intimate of George Washington and took active part in the creation of the United States. He published "My Days Have Been So Wondrous Free" in a collection of seven songs dedicated to George Washington in 1778. Washington wrote to Hopkinson from Mt. Vernon on February 5, 1789:

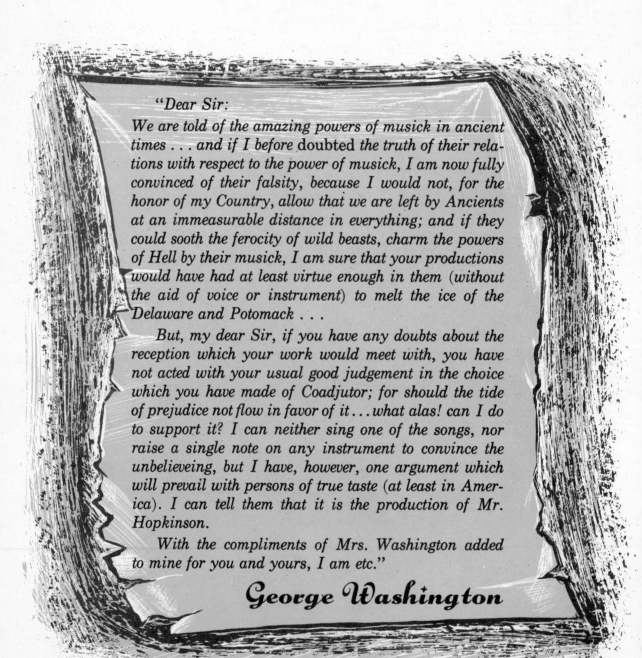

"Dear Sir:

We are told of the amazing powers of musick in ancient times . . . and if I before doubted the truth of their relations with respect to the power of musick, I am now fully convinced of their falsity, because I would not, for the honor of my Country, allow that we are left by Ancients at an immeasurable distance in everything; and if they could sooth the ferocity of wild beasts, charm the powers of Hell by their musick, I am sure that your productions would have had at least virtue enough in them (without the aid of voice or instrument) to melt the ice of the Delaware and Potomack . . .

But, my dear Sir, if you have any doubts about the reception which your work would meet with, you have not acted with your usual good judgement in the choice which you have made of Coadjutor; for should the tide of prejudice not flow in favor of it . . . what alas! can I do to support it? I can neither sing one of the songs, nor raise a single note on any instrument to convince the unbelieveing, but I have, however, one argument which will prevail with persons of true taste (at least in America). I can tell them that it is the production of Mr. Hopkinson.

With the compliments of Mrs. Washington added to mine for you and yours, I am etc."

George Washington

# THE GROWING COUNTRY:
# ON THE SEA
## 1790-1850

☆ ☆ ☆ ☆ ☆ ☆ ☆ ☆ ☆ ☆ ☆ ☆ ☆ ☆ ☆ ☆ ☆ ☆ ☆

Songs of the Sea and the War of 1812— Life on the sea, the attitude of the sailor, was reflected in song from earliest colonial times. There were simple songs about sailing, fishing and whaling, common to both the British and the colonial seaman, which because of the personal feeling or special information of their verses were probably sung mainly by men used to sea life. "Rolling Home," "The Whale," and "Maid of Amsterdam" fall into this category. Narrative story ballads about the sea were popular but not written specially for the sailor. He sang the sea story ballad just as he would sing any current song, for entertainment during those few hours aboard ship when he had leisure. These songs, "The *Golden Vanity*," "Henry Martin," or "High Barbaree," were as familiar to the American sailor as to the colonial seaman, for the American sailor was only the English-speaking sailor with a new national flag.

As we have seen, the American Revolutionary War had its quota of sea songs that reflected events with an immediacy that prose reports can never have. The same is true of the War of 1812, which was particularly rich in songs about the sea. Since it was a war fought over seaman's rights, since it was a war of land reverses and sea victories for America, it follows that the songs about this war sung during the war are ballads of fights at sea: "The *Constitution* and the *Guerrière*," "The *Hornet* and the *Peacock*." The other songs of the war did not come until later when there was an upsurge of patriotic feeling after the war was over. "Ye Parliaments of England" and "The Patriotic Diggers" fall into this group, along with several new boastful versions of the always present "Yankee Doodle."

The Chanty: Work Songs of the Sea— The most successful privateer design of the War of 1812 was the Baltimore Clipper. Similar clipper ships established the supremacy of American merchant shipping that lasted until supplanted by steam after 1850. These fast-sailing clipper ships called for crew teamwork. The necessity for group action led to an accented work song whose subject matter was some aspect of the life of the sailor and whose function was to insure smooth group action. This work song is called 127 the chanty. The word "chanty" (pronounced, and often spelled, "shanty") is said to have had its origin in the word "chant," used in the early 1800's to designate nonreligious and Negro singing.

The chanty worked in this way. The song was called out by a lead singer, the chantyman. He sang out the verses and set the tempo for the job and the men joined in on the chorus. The emphasized words in the chorus were co-ordinated with a pull or heave which was to accomplish the work. The chanties were meant to amuse as well as help in the work and each chantyman made up verses according to his ingenuity. He sang about sailing, fishing, war, love . . . anything and everything. A remembered verse from one boat was sung on another or in the taverns, and so these work songs of the sea were passed on and changed, showing the vitality of this kind of development.

Different rhythms were necessary for different kinds of shipboard work, and the chanties can be grouped in the following way:

Capstan chanties—A ship rode to many fathoms of chain cable, one end of which was fastened to a wheel on the deck, the capstan. Bars could be inserted in the capstan like the spokes of a wheel. To raise the anchor the men would man these spokes and start walking around and around, turning the capstan which pulled up the anchor and eventually brought it onto the deck. Chanties for this work were sung at a moderate tempo suited to the slow turning of the capstan.

Halyard chanties—The yards and the sheets had to be pulled up and the pace at which this was done depended upon whether the men were fresh or weary and the increasing weight of the pull.

Pumping chanties—The pumps usually stood amidships, and wooden vessels had to be pumped a little each day. Almost any chanty except the very short haul could be adapted to this work.

Short haul chanties—Any work that needed a series of quick, sharp pulls used this type of song.

Fishing and Whaling—Fishing and whaling, New England occupations from the very first, continued comparatively unchanged through the first half of the nineteenth century, even though the boats went farther afield, to the South Pacific and Alaskan waters. The big change took place on the clipper boats. After 1820, due to bad conditions, the big ships were largely deserted by native Americans who found better pay ashore or went west. Press gangs and boarding masters rounded up all kinds of jailbirds, greenhorns from the farms, and drunks, to make up the crews. The sailors who went back year after year to sea, in spite of the ill-treatment they received, were known as "packet rats." They were famous for their hard living and drunkenness, and it was to them the chanties belonged.

Tough as were the captains of the clipper ships, their respect and admiration for their boats was unqualified. One, Captain George Little, described his current command as follows: "Once more then, I am in command of one of the most beautiful models of a vessel that ever floated on the ocean—I mean a Baltimore Clipper schooner, of one hundred and forty tons burden, with proportions as scrupulously exact as if turned out of a mold. The workmanship was in all respects as neatly executed as if intended as a beautiful specimen of cabinet excellence; her spars were in perfect symmetry of proportions with the hull, and she sat upon the water like the seabird that sleeps at ease on the mountain billow. She was well armed and well manned, and, like some aerial being, as report had it, would at my call outstrip the wind."

# The Maid of Amsterdam

*This song, first appearing in 1608 in a London play by Thomas Heywood—"The Rape of Lucrece"—became very popular with colonial sailors.*

**Steady, in 2**

1. In Am-ster-dam there lived a maid, mark you well what I
2. I took this maid out for a walk, mark you well what I

say, in Am-ster-dam there lived a maid and
say, I took this maid out for a walk, __

she was mis-tress of her trade.
we had such a love-ly talk. I'll go no more a-

CHORUS:

rov - ing with you, fair maid. A - rov - ing, a -
rov - ing, since rov - ing's been my ru - i - in, I'll
go no more a rov - ing with you, fair maid.

3. Her eyes were blue, her cheeks
   were brown,
Mark you well what I say,
Her eyes were blue, her cheeks
   were brown,
Her hair in ringlets hanging down.

   *Chorus*

4. I took her out and spent my pay,
Mark you well what I say,
I took her out and spent my pay,
And then this maiden just faded
   away.

   *Chorus*

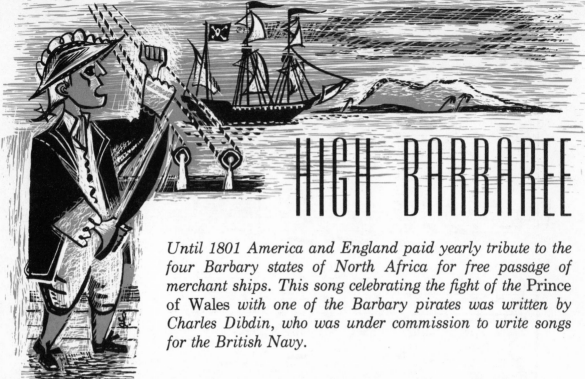

# HIGH BARBAREE

*Until 1801 America and England paid yearly tribute to the four Barbary states of North Africa for free passage of merchant ships. This song celebrating the fight of the* Prince of Wales *with one of the Barbary pirates was written by* Charles Dibdin, *who was under commission to write songs for the British Navy.*

Steady, in 2

1. There were two loft-y ships from_ old Eng-land
2. "A - loft_ there, a - loft!" our_ jol-ly boat-swain

came, blow high, blow low, and so_ sailed we; one
cried, blow high, blow low, and so_ sailed we; "look a -

was the Prince of Lu-ther, and the oth-er, Prince of
head,— look a - stern,— look a -weath-er, look a -

Wales, down a-long the coast of High Bar-ba - ree.
lee, cruis-ing down the coast of High Bar-ba - ree."

3. "There's naught upon the stern, there is naught upon the lee."
   Blow high, blow low, and so sailéd we;
   "But there's a lofty ship to windward, a sailing fast and free
   Down along the coast of High Barbaree."

4. "I'm not a man-o-war, nor a privateer," said he,
   Blow high, blow low, and so sailéd we;
   "But I am a salt-sea pirate, a-looking for my prey
   Down along the coast of High Barbaree."

5. Oh, 'twas broadside to broadside a long time we lay,
   Blow high, blow low, and so sailéd we;
   Until the Prince of Luther shot the Pirate's masts away,
   Down along the coast of High Barbaree.

6. "Oh, mercy, oh, mercy," those pirates then did cry,
   Blow high, blow low, and so sailéd we;
   But the mercy that we gave them—we sunk them in the sea,
   Down along the coast of High Barbaree.

# THE PIRATE SONG

*A picture of the romantic gentleman pirate, such as Lafitte of New Orleans, written in a sentimental mood.*

1. My boat's by the tow-er, and my bark's on the bay, and
2. For - give my rough mood un - ac - cus - tomed to sue; I

both must be gone at the dawn of the day. The
woo not, per - haps, as your land - lub - bers do. My

moon's in her shroud, and to light thee a - far on the
voice is at - tuned to the sound of the gun that

deck of the dar-ing's a love-light-ed star.
star-tles the deep when the com-bat's be-gun. So,

CHORUS:

wake, la-dy, wake, I am wait-ing for thee, oh, this night or

nev-er my bride thou shalt be, so, bride thou shalt be.

3. The Frenchman and Don will flee
    from our path,
And the Englishman cower below
    at our wrath,
And our sails shall be gilt
    in the gold of the day,
And the sea robins sing as we
    roll on our way.

*Chorus*

4. A hundred shall serve—the best
    of the brave—
And the chief of a thousand
    shall kneel as thy slave,
And thou shalt reign queen,
    and thy empire shall last
Till the black flag by inches
    is torn from the mast.

*Chorus*

135.

# THE CONSTITUTION AND THE GUERRIERE

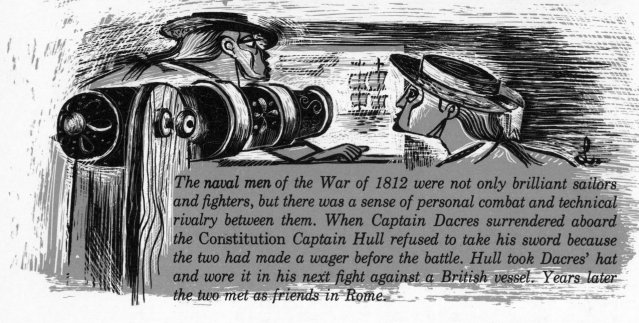

*The naval men of the War of 1812 were not only brilliant sailors and fighters, but there was a sense of personal combat and technical rivalry between them. When Captain Dacres surrendered aboard the Constitution Captain Hull refused to take his sword because the two had made a wager before the battle. Hull took Dacres' hat and wore it in his next fight against a British vessel. Years later the two met as friends in Rome.*

Free in delivery

1. It oft-times has been told that the
2. The Guer-riere, a frig-ate bold, on the
3. When this frig-ate hove in view, says proud

Brit-ish sea-men bold could flog the tars of
foam-y o-cean rolled, com-mand-ed by proud
Da-cres to his crew, "Come, clear the ship for

136.

France so neat and hand-y, oh! — But they nev-er found their
Da - cres the gran-dee, oh! — With as choice a Brit - ish
ac - tion and be hand-y, oh! — To the weath-er gauge, boys,

match till the Yan-kees they did catch, oh the
crew as a ram-mer ev - er drew, they could
get her," and to make his men fight bet-ter, gave

Yan-kee boys for fight-ing are the dan-dy, oh! —
flog the French-men two to one so hand - y, oh! —
them to drink gun - pow - der mixed with bran-dy, oh! —

4. The British shot flew hot,
Which the Yankees answered not,
Till they got within the distance
They called handy, oh!

Now says Hull unto his crew,
"Boys, let's see what we can do,
If we take these boasting Britons
We're the dandy, oh!"

5. Then the first broadside we poured
Carried their mainmast by the board,
Which made this lofty frigate
Look abandoned, oh!
Then Dacres shook his head
And to his officers said,
"Lord, I didn't think those Yankees
Were so handy, oh!"

6. Our second told so well
That their fore and mizzen fell,
Which doused the royal ensign
Neat and handy, oh!
"By George," says he, "We're done!"
And they fired a lee gun,
While the Yankees struck up
Yankee Doodle Dandy, oh!

7. Then Dacres came on board
To deliver up his sword,
Loath was he to part with it,
It was so handy, oh!
"Oh, keep your sword," says Hull,
"Why it only makes you dull.
Cheer up, let's have a little
Bit of brandy, oh!"

The frigate, Constitution, *lasted through all the fights of the War of 1812. She had been launched in 1797, fought the Barbary pirates, and was in commission until 1830. By that time a sentimental public was calling her "Old Ironsides." In 1830 she was condemned and ordered to be broken up. Newspaper editors, led by Dr. Oliver Wendell Holmes of Boston, raised a great cry against the destruction of the ship. She had become a symbol. Her preservation became a cause célèbre. Dr. Holmes wrote a poem called "Old Ironsides;" few will fail to remember its familiar verses, starting with the line: "Ay, tear her tattered ensign down!"*

# The Hornet and the Peacock

*The victory of the American Hornet over the British Peacock greatly cheered an American public, gloomy after many land reverses. Later the Hornet barely got away from the 74-gun Cornwallis by throwing overboard all guns, lifeboats and other movable objects. Thus they escaped the feared British prisons.*

**With command (free in delivery)**

1. Ye Dem-os, at-tend, and ye Fed-er-als, too: I'll
CHO. "Sing hub-ber, O bub-ber, cried old Gran-ny Weal, "the
2. This bird it was bred in the land of King George, her
3. King George then says, "To A-mer-i-ca go; the

sing you a song that you all know is true, con-
Hor-net can tick-le the Brit-ish bird's tail! Her
feath-ers were fine and her tail ver-y large: she
Hor-net, the Wasp, is the Brit-ish king's foe: Pick them

140.

cern-ing the Hor-net, true stuff, I'll be bail, that
stings are all sharp, and they'll pierce with-out fail; suc -
spread forth her wings, like a ship in full sail, and
up, my dear bird, spread your wings to the gale." "But be-

rum-pled the Pea-cock and low-ered her tail.
cess to our na-vy!" cried old Gran-ny Weal.
prid-ed her-self in the size of her tail. (repeat Cho.)
ware of these in-sects," cries old Gran-ny Weal. (repeat Cho.)

4. Away flew this bird at the word of command,
   Her flight was directed to freedom's own land;
   The Hornet discovered her wings on the sail,
   And quickly determined to tickle her tail. *Chorus*

5. So at it they went, it was both pick and stick,
   The Hornet still working keen under her wing;
   "American insects," quoth she, "I'll be bail,
   Will humble the king bird and tickle her tail." *Chorus*

6. The Peacock now mortally under her wing
   Did feel the full force of the Hornet's sharp sting;
   She flattened her crest like a shoal on the whale,
   Sunk down by her side and lower'd her tail. *Chorus*

7. Success to brave Lawrence, who well knew the nest
   Where the Hornet and Wasp with honor still rest.
   We'll send them a force, and with skill, I'll be bail,
   Will humble King George and tickle his tail. *Chorus*

# YE PARLIAMENTS OF ENGLAND

*This song is a nice summary of American hopes in mid-war. Perry had recouped American losses on Lake Erie and, as we see in the last stanza, the songwriter still thought it possible for us to acquire Canada. This was before Napoleon's capture freed the British fleets and troops for the landing in America that led to the burning of Washington, D. C.*

In 2, like a march

1. Ye par-lia-ments of Eng-land, ye Lords and Com-mons,
2. You first con-fined our com-merce: you said our ships shan't

too,— con - sid - er well what you're a - bout, and
trade,— and then im-pressed our sea - men, and

3. You thought our frigates were but few, and Yankees could not fight,
   Until brave Hull your Guerrière took and banished her from sight.
   You're now at war with Yankees; I'm sure you'll rue the day
   You roused the sons of liberty in North Americay.

4. Grant us free trade and commerce, don't you impress our men,
   Give up all claim to Canada, then we'll make peace again.
   Then, England, we'll respect you, and treat you as a friend.
   Respect our flag and citizens, then all these wars will end.

# THE PATRIOTIC DIGGERS

*A war song by Samuel Woodward, composer of "The Old Oaken Bucket."*

**Medium, in 2**

1. En - e - mies, be - ware, keep a prop - er dis - tance,
   To pro - tect our rights 'gainst your flint and trig - gers
2. Schol - ars leave their schools with pa - tri - ot - ic teach-ers,
   Bright A - pol - lo's sons leave their pipe and ta - bor,

else we'll make you stare at our firm re - sis - tance;
see on yon - der heights our pa - tri - ot - ic dig - gers.
farm-ers seize their tools, head - ed by their preach-ers,
mid the roar of guns join the mar - tial la - bor,

let a - lone the lads who are free-dom tast - ing,
Men of ev - 'ry age, col - or, rank, pro - fes - sion,
how they break the soil — brew-ers, butch-ers, bak - ers —
round the em-bat-tled plain in sweet con-cord ral - ly,

144.

don't for- get, our dads     gave you once a bast- ing.
ar -dent- ly en -gaged,     la - bor in suc - ces - sion.
here the doc- tors toil,     there the un - der - tak - ers.
and in free-dom's strain     sing the foe's fi - na - le.

CHORUS:

Pick-axe, shov- el,    spade,    crow-bar, hoe, and bar-row,

bet- ter not in - vade,     Yan-kees have the mar-row.

3. Better not invade, don't forget the spirit
   Which our dads displayed and their sons inherit.
   If you still advance, friendly caution slighting,
   You may get by chance a bellyful of fighting!
   Plumbers, founders, dyers, tinmen, turners, shavers,
   Sweepers, clerks, and criers, jewelers and engravers,
   Clothiers, drapers, players, cartmen, hatters, tailors,
   Gaugers, sealers, weighers, carpenters and sailors!

*Chorus*

# MISS BAILEY'S GHOST

*Traditional: sixteenth century.*

**Steady, in 2**

1. A cap-tain bold in Hal - i - fax, who dwelt in coun - try quar-ters, ___ se - duced a maid who hanged her - self one morn-ing in her gar - ters. ___ His wick- ed con-science
2. One night, be-times he went to bed, for he had caught a fe - ver, ___ said he, "I am a hand-some man and I'm a gay de - ceiv - er." ___ His can-dle just at

smit-ed him, he lost his stom-ach dai-ly,_____ he
twelve o'-clock be-gan to burn quite pale-ly,_____ a

took to drink-ing tur-pen-tine and thought up-on Miss Bai-ley._
ghost stepped up to his bed-side and said, "Be-hold! Miss Bai-ley."_

CHORUS:

Oh, Miss Bai-ley, un-for-tun-ate Miss Bai-ley, Bai-ley.

3. "Avaunt, Miss Bailey," then he cried, "you can't affright me really."
"Dear Captain Smith," the ghost replied, "you've used me ungenteelly.
The Coroner's quest was hard with me because I've acted frailly,
And parson Biggs won't bury me though I'm a dead Miss Bailey."
*Chorus*

4. "Dear Ma'am," said he, "since you and I accounts must once for all close,
I have a one-pound note in my regimental small clothes.
'Twill bribe the Sexton for your grave." The ghost then vanished gaily,
Crying, "Bless you wicked Captain Smith, remember poor Miss Bailey."
*Chorus*

147.

# THE HUNTERS OF KENTUCKY

*Samuel Woodward wrote this song in 1830, using the melody of
Miss Bailey's Ghost for verses about the Battle of New Orleans.*

1. Ye gentlemen and ladies fair,
   Who grace this famous city,
   Just listen if you've time to spare,
   While I rehearse a ditty:
   And for the opportunity
   Conceive yourselves quite lucky,
   For 'tis not often that you see
   A hunter from Kentucky.
   > Oh Kentucky, the hunters of Kentucky!
   > Oh Kentucky, the hunters of Kentucky!

2. We are a hardy, free-born race,
   Each man to fear a stranger:
   Whate'er the game we'll join the chase,
   Despoiling time and danger,
   And if a daring foe annoys
   Whate'er his strength and forces,
   We'll show him that Kentucky boys
   Are alligator horses.
   > Oh Kentucky, the hunters of Kentucky!
   > Oh Kentucky, the hunters of Kentucky!

3. You've heard I s'pose how New Orleans
   Is famed for wealth and beauty,
   There's girls of every hue it seems
   From snowy white to sooty.
   So Pakenham he made his brags,
   If he in fight was lucky,
   He'd have their girls and cotton bags,
   In spite of old Kentucky.
   > Oh Kentucky, the hunters of Kentucky!
   > Oh Kentucky, the hunters of Kentucky!

4. But Jackson he was wide awake
   And was not scar'd at trifles,
   For well he knew what aim we take
   With our Kentucky rifles.
   So he led us down to cypress swamp,
   The ground was low and mucky,
   There stood John Bull in martial pomp
   And here was old Kentucky.
   > Oh Kentucky, the hunters of Kentucky!
   > Oh Kentucky, the hunters of Kentucky!

# YANKEE DOODLE (1812)

*This survey of the War of 1812 appeared soon after the Battle
of New Orleans, celebrating the successful end of hostilities.*

1. The wars are o'er and
     peace is come,
   Our foes away are far gone;
   We sent the Britons striking home,
   And flogged 'em in the bargain.

   *Chorus:*

   Yankee Doodle is the tune,
   It comes so nation handy,
   And nothing makes a Briton run
   Like Yankee Doodle Dandy!

2. They first attacked and thought
     to crush
   Our gallant little navy;
   But Yankee tars soon stopped
     their grog,
   And sent 'em to old Davy!

   *Chorus*

3. The foes next tried our boys ashore,
   Their Sirs and Lords commanded,
   But pretty soon they found
     themselves
   All Yankee Doodle Dandyed!

   *Chorus*

4. Immortal Pike first shipped
     his troops,
   Upon the lake, at Sackets;
   He sought and found the foe
     at York,
   And dusted well their jackets!

   *Chorus*

5. The hero there laid down his life,
   To raise his country's glory;
   As all our sons will pant to do,
   Whene'er they hear the story.

   *Chorus*

6. Our gallant Pearce then
     took command,
   And stormed the fortress handy;
   Our STARS were hoisted to
     the tune
   Of Yankee Doodle Dandy!

   *Chorus*

7. Brave Brown and Scott next taught
     the foe,
   And taught 'em mighty quick, sirs,
   That we had still kept up the bread
   Of our old Seventy-Sixers!

   *Chorus*

8. The foe at last being tired out,
   With many a hearty thrashing,
   They all went down to
     New Orleans,
   And thought to get possession.

   *Chorus*

9. The veteran troops who
     conquered Spain
   Thought that our folks would
     vanish;
   But JACKSON settled half
     their men,
   And made the rest walk Spanish.

   *Chorus*

10. Then keep the bottle full, my boys,
    And keep it in rotation;
    We'll drink a health to those
      that fought
    The battles of our nation.

    *Chorus*

# BLOW THE MAN DOWN

*This is the classic topsail halyard chanty. The Black Ball line of which it speaks was founded by a group of Quakers in 1818, and was the first line to take passengers on regular scheduled sailings. These ships soon became famous for quick passages, fighting mates, and the way in which both ship and crew were driven. The use of fists, belaying pins, and flogging was common, and the packets got the name of "Red Hot Blood Ships." "Kicking Jack" Williams was an actual captain of the day.*

1. Come all ye young fel-lows that fol-low the sea, to my way haye, blow the man down, and

2. I'm a deep wa-ter sail-or just in from Hong Kong, to my way haye, blow the man down, if you'll

pray, pay at - ten - tion and lis - ten to me,
give me some grog, — I'll sing you a song,

give me some time to blow the man down.
give me some time to blow the man down.

3. 'Twas on a Black Baller I first served my time,
And on that Black Baller I wasted my prime.

4. 'Tis when a Black Baller's preparing for sea
You'd split your sides laughing at sights that you see.

5. With the tinkers and tailors and soljers and all
That ship for prime seamen on board a Black Ball.

6. 'Tis when a Black Baller is clear of the land,
Our Boatswain then gives us the word of command.

7. "Lay aft," is the cry, "to the break of the Poop!
Or I'll help you along with the toe of my boot!"

8. 'Tis larboard and starboard on the deck you will sprawl,
For "Kicking Jack" Williams commands the Black Ball.

9. Pay attention to orders, now you one and all,
For right there above you flies the Black Ball.

# AWAY, RIO

*A capstan chanty; referring to the South American trade.*

Waltz

Eb

1. The an-chor is weigh'd, and the sails they are set. A-way—
2. So it's pack up your don-key and get un-der way. A-way—
3. We've a jol-ly good ship and a jol-ly good crew. A-way—
4. We'll sing as we heave to the maid-ens we leave. A-way—
5. Heave with a will,— and heave long and strong. A-way—
6. The chains up and down now, the bo-sun did say, A-way—

Eb        Ab        Eb        Bb7        Eb

— Ri-o. — The maids we are leav-ing we'll nev-er for-get,
— Ri-o. — The girls we are leav-ing can take half our pay,
— Ri-o. — A jol-ly good mate and a good skip-per too,
— Ri-o. — And you who are lis-ten-ing, good-bye to you,
— Ri-o. — Sing the good chor-us, for 'tis a good song,
— Ri-o. — Heave up the hawse pipe, the an-chors a-weigh,

and we're bound for the Ri-o— Grande, and a - way—

— Ri-o,——— a - way—

Ri-o,——— we're bound—a - way— on this ver-y

day, yes, we're bound for the Ri-o— Grande.—

153.

# SHENANDOAH

*A short haul chanty.*

Slow (free in delivery)

1. The old Miz-zoo,___ she's a might-y riv-er.___
2. The white man loved___ an In-dian maid-en.___

'Way ___ you roll-ing riv-er! ___ The
'Way ___ you roll-ing riv-er! ___ With

In-dians camp a-long her bor-der.___
no-tions his ca-noe was la-den.___ A-

154.

way _____ we're bound, a - way,  'cross the wide _____ Mis - sou - ri. _____

3. Oh, Shenandoah, I love your daughter,
   'Way you rolling river,
   I'll take her 'cross your rolling water,
   Away, we're bound away, across the wide Missouri.

4. The Chief disdained the trader's dollars,
   'Way you rolling river,
   My daughter you shall never follow,
   Away, we're bound away, across the wide Missouri.

5. At last there came a Yankee skipper,
   'Way you rolling river,
   He winked his eye and he tipped his flipper,
   Away, we're bound away, across the wide Missouri.

6. He sold the chief that firewater,
   'Way you rolling river,
   And 'cross that river he stole his daughter,
   Away, we're bound away, across the wide Missouri.

7. Fare you well, I'm bound to leave you,
   'Way you rolling river,
   Oh Shenandoah I'll not deceive you,
   Away, we're bound away, across the wide Missouri.

155.

# The Drunken Sailor

*A capstan chanty. On the words "Way Hay and Up She Rises," the men would stamp loudly on the decks. This led to a whole category of songs known as "stamp and go" chanties.*

Way, hay, up she ris-es, Way, hay, up she ris-es,

Way, hay, up she ris-es ear-lye in the morn-ing!

1. What will we do with the drunk-en sail-or?
2. Put him in the scup-pers with the hose pipe on him,

3. Put him in the scuppers with the hose-pipe on him.

4. Hoist him aboard with a running bowline.

5. Put him in the brig until he's sober.

6. Make him turn to at shining bright work.

# HULLABALOO BELAY

*Shallo Brown was a notorious boarding-house keeper. He lodged sailors, taking three months' pay in advance and working as agent to provide forced crews. Back afloat, the sailors called the first three months "working off the dead horse."*

**Easy-going, in 2**

1. My moth-er kept a board-ing house,
2. A fresh young fel-low named Shal-lo Brown,

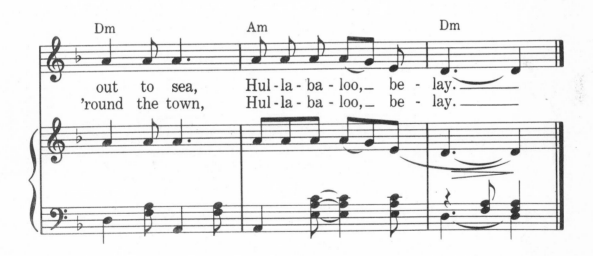

3. One day when father was on the crown
Me mother ran off with Shallo Brown.

4. Me father says, "Young man, me b'y,"
To which I quickly made reply,

5. Me father slowly pined away,
Because me mother came back the next day.

# Haul Away Joe

*A short haul chanty.*

mold - y.___
tu - tion.___ Way, haul a-way, we'll haul a-way Joe.___
bran - dy.___

CHORUS:

Way, haul a-way, we'll haul for bet-ter weath -

er,___ way, haul a-way, we'll haul a-way Joe. 2. King Joe.
3. Oh, the

# SACRAMENTO

*A chanty based on Stephen Foster's minstrel song, "Camp Town Races."*

Comfortable, in 2

1. Sing and heave, and heave and sing, doo da,
2. Round Cape Horn in the months of snow, doo da,

doo da, heave and make the hand spikes ring, hoo, doo da
doo da, if we get there no one knows, hoo, doo da

162.

CHORUS:

day. Then blow the winds, hi ho, for Cal - i - for - ni - o, for there's plen-ty of gold, so I've been told, on the banks of the Sa - cra - men - to.

3. A bully ship and a bully crew,
   A bully mate and a captain too.

   *Chorus*

4. From Limehouse Docks to Sidney Head
   Was never more than seventy days.

   *Chorus*

5. We cracked it on, a big skiute,
   And the old man felt like a swell galoot.

   *Chorus*

# ROLLING HOME

*A forecastle song and capstan chanty.*

**Steady, with feeling**

1. Up a - loft, a - mid the rig - ging swift - ly blows the fa - v'ring gale, strong as spring - time in its blos - som, fill - ing out each bend - ing sail, and the
2. Now, it takes all hands to man the cap - stan, Mis - ter, see your ca - bles clear! Soon you'll be sail - ing home - ward bound, sir, and for the chan - nel you will steer. See your
3. Full ten thous - and miles be - hind us, and a thous - and miles be - fore, an - cient o - cean waves to waft us to the well - re - mem - bered shore. New - born

waves we leave be-hind us seem to mur-mur as they rise: we have
sheets and crew-lines free, sir, all your bunt-lines o-ver-hauled; are the
breez-es swell to send us to our child-hood wel-come skies, to the

tar - ried here to bear you to the land you dear-ly prize.
sheer-poles and gear all read-y? Soon for New Eng-land we will steer.
glow of friend-ly fac- es and the glance of lov-ing eyes.

CHORUS:

Roll-ing_ home, roll-ing home, roll-ing home, a-cross the sea, roll-ing

home to dear old Eng-land, roll-ing home,_ dear_ land, to thee.

# Blow Ye Winds

*A forecastle song about whaling ships and their crews.*

Comfortable, in 2

1. 'Tis ad-ver-tised in Bos-ton, New York and Buf-fa-lo, five hun-dred brave A-mer-i-cans a-whal-ing for to go,— sing-ing: Blow, ye winds, in the
2. They send you to New Bed-ford, a fa-mous whal-ing port, and give you to some land-sharks to board and fit you out,— sing-ing: Blow, ye winds, in the

CHORUS:

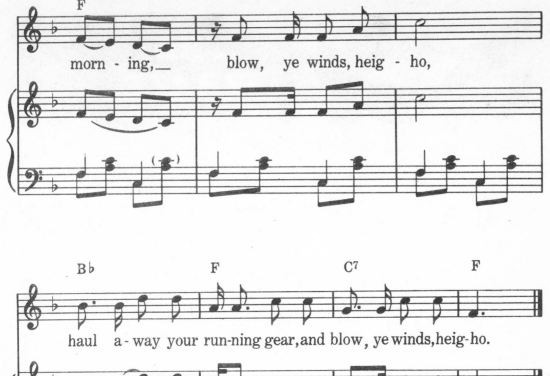

morn - ing, ___ blow, ye winds, heig - ho,

haul a - way your run-ning gear, and blow, ye winds, heig-ho.

3. They tell you of the clipper-ships a-running in and out,
   And say you'll take five hundred sperm before you're
   six months out, singing

   *Chorus*

4. And now we're out to sea, my boys, the wind comes on to blow;
   One half the watch is sick on deck, the other half below, singing

   *Chorus*

5. The Skipper's on the quarterdeck a-squintin' at the sails,
   When up above the lookout sights a mighty school of whales, singing

   *Chorus*

6. Then lower down the boats, my boys, and after him we'll travel,
   But if you get too near his fluke he'll kick you to the devil, singing

   *Chorus*

7. And now that he is ours, my boys, we'll tow him alongside;
   Then over with our blubber-hooks and rob him of his hide, singing

   *Chorus*

167.

# THE WHALE

Definite, in 4

1. It was in the year of for-ty-four, in March, the sec - ond day, that our gal-lant ship her anchors weighed, and for
2. And when we came to far Green-land, to Green-land cold we came, where there is frost and there is snow, and the

sea they bore — a - way, brave boys, and for
might - y whale-fish-es blow, brave boys, and the

*slower*

sea they bore — a - way.
might - y whale - fish - es blow.

*slower*

3. Our bosun went to topmast high
   With his spyglass in his hand.
   "There's a whale! There's a whale!
   There's a whalefish," he cried,
   "And she blows at every span, brave boys,
   And she blows at every span."

4. Our captain stood on the quarterdeck,
   And a brave little man was he,
   "Overhaul, overhaul, on your davit tackles fall,
   And launch your boats for sea, brave boys,
   And launch your boats for sea."

5. We struck the whale, and away we went,
   And he lashed out with his tail,
   And we lost the boat and five good men,
   And we never got that whale, brave boys,
   And we ne'er did get that darn whale.

6. Oh Greenland is an awful place
   Where the daylight's seldom seen,
   Where there is frost and there is snow,
   And the mighty whalefishes blow, brave boys,
   And the mighty whalefishes blow.

# Song of the Fishes

*A forecastle fishing song.*

Waltz, steady rhythm

1. Come all ye bold Fish-er-men, lis-ten to me, I'll
2. First comes the blue fish a wag-ging his tail, he

sing you a song of the fish in the sea. So
comes up on deck and yells: "All hands make sail!"

CHORUS:

blow, ye winds, wes-ter-ly, wes-ter-ly blow,—we're

170.

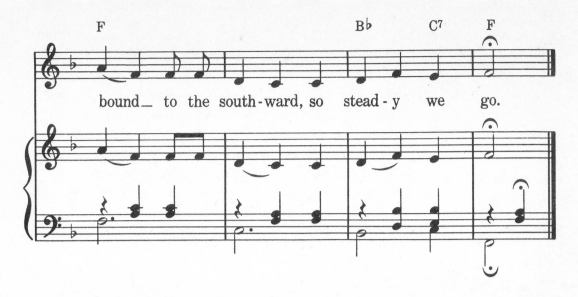

bound — to the south-ward, so stead-y we go.

3. Next come the eels with their nimble tails,
   They jumped up aloft and loosed all the sails.

4. Next come the herrings with their little tails,
   They manned sheets and halyards and set all the sails.

5. Next comes the porpoise with his short snout,
   He jumps on the bridge and yells: "Ready, about!"

6. Next comes the swordfish, the scourge of the sea,
   The order he gives is: "Helm's a-lee!"

7. Then comes the turbot, as red as a beet,
   He shouts from the bridge: "Stick out that foresheet!"

8. Having accomplished these wonderful feats,
   The blackfish sings out next to: "Rise tacks and sheets!"

9. Next comes the whale, the largest of all,
   Singing out from the bridge: "Haul taut, mainsail, haul!"

10. Then comes the mackerel with his striped back,
    He flopped on the bridge and yelled: "Board the main tack!"

11. Next comes the sprat, the smallest of all,
    He sings out: "Haul well taut, let go and haul!"

12. Then comes the catfish with his chucklehead,
    Out in the main chains for a heave of the lead.

13. Next comes the flounder, quite fresh from the ground,
    Crying: "Damn your eyes, chucklehead, mind where you sound!"

14. Along came the dolphin, flapping his tail,
    He yelled to the boatswain to reef the foresail.

15. Along came the shark with his three rows of teeth,
    He flops on the foreyard and takes a snug reef.

16. Up jumps the fisherman, stalwart and grim,
    And with his big net he scoops them all in.

# The Dreadnought

*Known as "The Wild Boat of the Atlantic," the Dread-nought still holds the transatlantic speed record for sailing ships. Launched at Newburyport in 1853, flying the flag of the Red Cross Line, she was typical of the finest clipper ships. She sailed in the Atlantic and China trade in all weather and went down while doubling Cape Horn in 1869.*

Steady

1. There's a sau-cy wild pack-et, and a pack-et of fame; she be-longs to New York, and The
2. The time of her sail-ing is__ now draw-ing nigh; fare-well, pret-ty May, I must

3. Oh, the Dreadnought is pulling out of Waterlock dock,
   Where the boys and the girls to the pierheads do flock;
   They will give us three cheers while their tears do flow,
   Saying, "God bless the Dreadnought, where'er she may go!"

# THE DREADNOUGHT

4. Oh, the Dreadnought is waiting in the Mersey so free,
   Waiting for the Independence to tow her to sea,
   For around that rock light where the Mersey does flow,
   Bound away in the Dreadnought, to the westward we'll go.

5. Oh, the Dreadnought's a-bowlin' down the wild Irish Sea,
   Where the passengers are merry, their hearts full of glee,
   While her sailors like lions walk the decks to and fro,
   She's the Liverpool packet, oh, Lord, let her go!

6. Oh, the Dreadnought's a-sailin' the Atlantic so wide,
   While the dark, heavy seas roll along her black sides,
   With her sails neatly spread and the Red Cross to show,
   She's the Liverpool packet, oh, Lord, let her go!

7. Oh, the Dreadnought's becalmed on the banks of Newfoundland,
   Where the water's so green and the bottom is sand;
   Where the fish of the ocean swim round to and fro,
   She's the Liverpool packet, oh, Lord, let her go!

8. Oh, the Dreadnought, she's a-bowlin' past old Nantucket Head,
   And the man in the chains takes a cast with the lead,
   Then up jumps the flounder just fresh from the ground,
   Crying, "Blast your eyes, Chucklehead; and mind where you sound!"

9. Oh, the Dreadnought's arrived in America once more,
   We'll go ashore, shipmates, on the land we adore,
   See our wives and our sweethearts, be merry and free,
   Drink a health to the Dreadnought, wheresoe'er she may be.

10. Here's a health to the Dreadnought, and to all her brave crew.
    Here's a health to her captain and officers, too.
    Talk about your flash packets, Swallow Tail and Black Ball,
    But the Dreadnought's the clipper to beat one and all.

Robert j. LEE

175.

# THE CROCODILE SONG

*A tall tale of the sea, set to an old Irish tune.*

Comfortable, in 2

1. Come, list ye, lands-men, all to me, to tell the truth I'm
   Ship-wrecked I was one sap-py rouse, and cast all on the
2. Oh! I had not long walked a-bout when close a-long-side the
   While steer-ing close be-side the thing, I saw it was a

bound. What hap-pened to me by
shore, so I re-solved to
o-cean,— 'twas there I saw
croc-o-dile, from the end of his nose to the

go-ing to the sea, and the won-ders that I found.
take a trip the coun-try to ex-plore.
some-thing move like all the earth in mo-tion.
tip of his tail he meas-ured five hun-dred mile.

CHORUS:

To my ri too-ral loo-ral lay, to my ri too-ral lay,—— to

my ri too-ral lid-dle lol de fol, to my ri too-ral lay.

3. This crocodile, I could plainly see,
   Was none of the common race,
   For I had to climb a very tall tree
   Before I could see his face.
   Up above the wind was high,
   It blew such a hard gale from
        the south
   That I let go my hold, you see,
   And fell into the crocodile's mouth.

   *Chorus:*
   To my ri too-ra loo-ra lay,
   To my ri too-ra lay,
   To my ri too-ra liddle lol li fol,
   To my ri too-ra lay.

4. He quickly closed his jaws on me,
   He thought to nab a victim;
   But I slipped down his throat,
        you see,
   That's the way I tricked him.

   *Chorus*

5. I traveled on for a year or two,
   Till I got into his maw,
   And there were rum cakes not
        a few
   And a thousand pullets in store.
   Right then I banished all my cares,
   For grub I was not stinted;
   And in this crocodile I lived
        ten years,
   Right very well contented

   *Chorus*

6. This crocodile being very old
   At last at length he died,
   He was six months in catching
        cold,
   He was so long and wide.
   His skin was ten mile thick,
        I think,
   Or very near about;
   For I was fully six months or so
   In a-digging my way out.

   *Chorus*

177.

# RELIGIOUS, PROFESSIONAL AND FOLK SINGING

## 1800-1850

☆ ☆ ☆ ☆ ☆ ☆ ☆ ☆ ☆ ☆ ☆ ☆ ☆ ☆ ☆ ☆ ☆ ☆ ☆ ☆ ☆

After the Revolutionary War a growing number of songs were composed in the United States: anonymous ballads, hymns, and professional songs for the entertainment field. These songs were taken up by the people and sung apart from any printed copies so that the imagination and memory of the singers worked on the songs to develop them into American folk songs.

Religious Folk Songs— There was a major revival in hymn singing after 1800 and great creative energy went into the writing and singing of new hymns. Many books of songs, hymns, and spirituals were published, composed by such men as Isaac Watts and Lowell Mason in the field of traditional church music. In the less formal field of open church meetings, which so quickly became a part of frontier and southern life, Singing Billy Walker became the important composer.

Singing Billy, born a Welshman, published in 1835 a book called "The Southern Harmony and Musical Companion," containing 334 songs. Most of these songs were written in a minor mode. They were the songs that the colored slaves were taught by their southern masters, and they became the basis, it is believed, for the Negro spiritual. Singing Billy's book was the one used by the itinerant revival preachers.

While the church revival meeting with its rhythm singing was much deplored by the more formal clergymen, it was for a long time the basis of the only religious life that came to the frontier. The influence of the itinerant preacher and of song is nicely portrayed in the following account of a revival meeting attended by Dr. Alexander, professor at Princeton Theological Seminary, just before 1850.

> When the preacher came to the application of his discourse, he became exceedingly vehement and boisterous; and I could hear some sounds in the centre of the house which indicated strong emotion. At length a female voice was heard in a piercing cry, which thrilled through me, and affected the whole audience.

In a few seconds one and another rose in different parts of the house, in extreme and visible agitation. . . . Here I saw the power of sympathy. The feeling was real, and was propagated from person to person by mere sound. The feelings expressed were different; for while some uttered the cry of poignant anguish, others shouted in the accents of triumph.

The speaker's voice was soon silenced, and he sat down and gazed on the scene with a complacent smile. When this tumult had lasted a few minutes, another preacher began to sing a soothing yet lively tune, and was quickly joined by some strong female voices near him; and in less than two minutes the storm was hushed, and there was a great calm. I experienced the most sensible relief to my own feelings from the appropriate music . . .

Lowell Mason of Boston—carrying on the tradition of William Billings in the field of hymns and religious songs—was in strong contrast to the revivalist groups. He published many collections of music, made translations and put original texts to old music, as well as composing many original melodies of his own. He is indirectly responsible for the writing of the patriotic hymn "America." He gave some German music books to the Reverend Smith, who became enthusiastic over a melody and wrote the words we now sing, not realizing that the melody had already been chosen by the British as their national anthem.

## Songs from the Entertainment Fields

Songs from the Entertainment Fields—After the War of 1812 professional American songwriters began to flourish. There was Samuel Woodworth who wrote the popular "Hunters of Kentucky" and many other songs dealing with the War of 1812. He wrote several songs celebrating the American visit of Lafayette in 1824 and is particularly well known for such successes as "The Deep Tangled Wildwood" and "The Old Oaken Bucket."

Another professional songwriter was the Englishman Henry Russell, who came to the United States as a touring concert singer and remained as first organist of the Presbyterian Church of Rochester, New York. His most famous songs are "Woodman, Spare that Tree," "The Old Arm Chair," and "Life on the Ocean Wave."

The most prolific and popular songwriters of the next generation, 1830-1850, were Henry Clay Work, George Root, and Stephen Foster. Their music was published as sheet music and widely sung on the variety and concert stages. There were, of course, other songwriters who gained popularity and wrote such successes as "We Won't Go Home Until Morning," "Rocked in the Cradle of the Deep," "The Hard Cider Quick Step," "Stop That Knocking at My Door" and "The Old Gum Tree," to name but a few that we still sing.

Beside the concert artists who traveled the country and popularized these songs, there were a considerable number of families who traveled together as troupes. Two of the most famous were the Hutchinson and the Baker families. Their family programs included solos, ensembles, and both vocal and instrumental pieces. Typical of the repertoire of the Hutchinson family were "The Old Granite State," "The Bachelor's Lament," "My Mother's Bible," "Man the Life Boat," and "The Spider and the Fly."

From the 1830's on, the vaudeville stage expanded rapidly, featuring comic songs on every kind of subject matter. There were "New York, Oh What a Charming City," "Buy a Broom," "The Cork Leg," "The Monkey's Wedding" ("The Monkey Married the Baboon's Sister"), "The Pesky Sarpint," and "Springfield Mountain." Bobbie Burns' songs and Dibdin's "Sea Songs" found their place too on the variety stage, and from there went into the homes and across country with the pioneers.

The most famous and best-remembered songs, however, come from the minstrel shows that became so popular after 1832. Thomas (Daddy) Rice was actually the first to start the black-faced tradition when he augmented his variety act by impersonating a Negro singer he had observed on the street. He changed the song he took from the Negro into a song and dance called "Jump, Jim Crow," which achieved tremendous popularity. This led to Negro characterizations by Rice and others and to many songs in Negro dialect.

In 1843, four of the greatest of the black-faced players combined as the Virginia Minstrels and went to New York with new instrumental and vocal effects that made a sensation at their debut at the Bowery Amphitheatre. There was Dan Emmett who played the fiddle, Billy Whitlock who played the banjo, Frank Brower who clacked bones at one end, and Dick Pelham who used a tambourine at the other. Their fast-moving program of songs, jokes, dances, and instrumental specialties with the use of Mr. Bones and Mr. Tambourine as end men and Mr. Interlocutor as middle man set the form for later minstrel shows. The Virginia Minstrels were immediately followed by other similar groups, perhaps the most famous of which were the Christy Minstrels and the Ethiopian Serenaders.

Many of these minstrel players wrote their own songs. Dan Emmett, the most famous, produced "Dixie," "Old Dan Tucker," and "The Blue Tail Fly." Many of Stephen Foster's best-known pieces were written for these traveling minstrel shows. There were few places the minstrel shows did not reach after the 1840's. As a result a great many of our country dance tunes and folk songs are based on songs originating with the minstrel groups.

Folk Ballads, Dances, and Songs—Immigration in America in the early nineteenth century meant the transplantation of many traditional songs from Europe. The Scots, Irish, and Germans who came over in such great numbers brought their traditional songs with them. These became a part of the singing in American communities, were learned by neighbors and moved with them from town to town. As time went on these songs were transmitted from person to person, from parent to child, to grandchild, with changes introduced by each. Often words or tune were changed. Sometimes the tune would be forgotten and a new one devised for the old story. Sometimes the tune would be remembered and a new story found to suit it. Then, too, new songs came to be written as the new country expanded. Some of these new songs were completely original, and some were variations of

180

old songs made to fit new conditions.

These new, or partially new, songs came out of the experiences the new country offered. There were children's songs, love songs, ballads and play songs. They had their source in the traditional songs, in minstrel and popular songs, in religious songs. There was a creative ferment and energy which found expression in singing and produced humor, beauty, anecdote, and social comment.

The British Country Dances and European folk dances found a place in the new country. All over the United States they learned the Contre Dances where two lines were formed and danced opposite each other. They learned the Quadrille, a drill in quadrangular formation, and Square Dances—done in square formation. They learned Jigs from Ireland, Reels from Scotland, Quadrilles from France, and Hornpipes from England. The dance manager, who called the steps of the dance, and the dancing master were in great demand.

The more religious communities, of which there were many, did not allow dancing. As a substitute, games became the social diversion. The games were group movements made to songs known as Play-party songs. After a time rhythmic popular songs like "Old Dan Tucker," "Buffalo Gals," "Zip Coon," were borrowed for this purpose. The songs were catchy and provided an easy verse form to which new lines could be made up.

For the record, let it not be thought that dancing was limited even in frontier towns to the Play-party games. A traveler in 1839 was shocked by the abandoned social gatherings of most Mississippi towns. However, he found ballroom dancing in St. Louis very prim. ". . . they frequently hold each other by the hand," he writes, "and the lady places her idle hand on her waist; while the gentleman flourishes his gracefully either above his own or his partner's head, or assigns to it some resting place no less extraordinary. In some circles in the South, elbow-waltzing alone is permitted; the lady's waist is forbidden ground, and the gentleman is compelled to hold her by the points of the elbows."

# THE WAYFARING STRANGER

*White Spiritual about 1800*

Melancholy waltz

I'm just a poor, __ way-far-ing stran-ger __ trav - 'ling through __ this world of woe, __

183.

# THE WAYFARING STRANGER

184.

-ing o-ver home.

The great religious revival in Kentucky, Tennessee, and the Carolinas brought forth many folk hymns whose subject matter was a personal religious experience. The religious revival meetings were just this. The first verse of this song, of a more general nature, is more often sung than the religious second and third verses:

I know dark clouds will gather round me,
I know my way is steep and rough,
But beauteous fields lie just beyond me
Where souls redeemed their vigil keep.
I'm going there to meet my mother,
She said she'd meet me when I come;
I'm only going over Jordan,
I'm only going over home.

I want to wear a crown of glory
When I get home to that bright land;
I want to shout Salvation's story,
In concert with that bloodwashed band.
I'm going there to meet my Saviour,
To sing his praise forever more;
I'm only going over Jordan,
I'm only going over home.

The first Camp Meeting was held in the year 1801. Presbyterians and Methodists together held a tremendous meeting in Kentucky which set the revival style. Here the custom of the Mourner's Bench where penitents publicly confessed their sins to the congregation and were prayed over was instituted.

# Nearer My God To Thee

*Words and music: Lowell Mason*

186.

near-er, my God, to Thee, near-er to Thee.

# Wondrous Love

*The two hymns on this page show two religious trends. "Wondrous Love," sung to the tune of "Captain Kidd" (p. 47), is a camp meeting hymn. "Nearer My God to Thee" is one of Lowell Mason's famous hymns for the established church.*

1. What wondrous love is this, oh! my soul, oh, my soul!
What wondrous love is this, oh my soul!
What wondrous love is this! that caused the Lord of bliss
To bear the dreadful curse for my soul, for my soul,
To bear the dreadful curse for my soul.

2. When I was sinking down, sinking down, sinking down;
When I was sinking down, sinking down;
When I was sinking down
Beneath God's righteous frown,
Christ laid aside his crown for my soul, for my soul;
Christ laid aside his crown for my soul.

3. And when from death I'm free, I'll sing on, I'll sing on,
And when from death I'm free, I'll sing on.
And when from death I'm free,
I'll sing and joyful be,
And through eternity I'll sing on, I'll sing on,
And through eternity I'll sing on.

4. To God and to the Lamb I will sing, I will sing,
To God and to the Lamb I will sing,
To God and to the Lamb, who is the great I Am,
While millions join the theme, I will sing, I will sing,
While millions join the theme, I will sing.

# The Turtle Dove

*During the time of Shakespeare, music was a necessary qualification for ladies and gentlemen. The "Turtle Dove" was at this time a symbol of love and Turtle Dove songs were current from the middle of the sixteenth century. Both the old colonial and the new settlers from the British Isles kept this symbol. This song seems to be of purely American origin except that the symbol of the English turtle dove is used.*

With feeling (free in delivery)

Poor lit-tle tur-tle dove, set-ting on a pine,

Long-ing for his own true love as I did once for

mine, for mine, as I did once for mine.

2. I come down the mountainside
   I give my horn a blow
   Everywhere them pretty girls
   Said yonder goes my beau, my beau,
   Yonder goes my beau.

3. I went down in the valley green
   To win to me my love,
   When I done with that pretty little girl
   She turned to a turtle dove, a dove,
   She turned to a turtle dove.

4. I walked down the street that very same night,
   On my heart was a sweet, sweet song
   Got in a fight and in jail all night
   And every durn thing went wrong, went wrong,
   Every durn thing went wrong.

5. I went up on the mountainside
   And I took a swig of corn,
   Possum wrapped his tail around a blackberry bush
   Two mountain lions were born, were born,
   Two mountain lions were born.

6. Poor little turtle dove,
   Setting on a pine,
   Longing for his own true love
   As I once did for mine, for mine,
   As I once did for mine.

# BILLY BOY

## (ENGLISH)

*There are two predominant versions of "Billy Boy," Irish and English.*

**In 2, not too fast**

1. Where have you been all the day, my boy Wil-lie?
2. Is she fit to be a wife, my boy Wil-lie?

Where have you been all the day, Wil-lie won't you tell me now?
Is she fit to be a wife, Wil-lie won't you tell me now?

I have been all the day court-in' of a la-dy gay,
She's as fit to be a wife as a fork fits to a knife,

but she is too young to be tak-en from her moth-er.
but she is too young to be tak-en from her moth-er.

3. Can she cook and can she spin, my boy Willie?
   Can she cook and can she spin, Willie won't you tell me now?
   She can cook, she can spin, she can do most anything,
   But she is too young to be taken from her mother.

4. Can she bake a cherry pie, my boy Willie?
   Can she bake a cherry pie, Willie won't you tell me now?
   She can bake a cherry pie, quick's a cat can wink his eye,
   But she is too young to be taken from her mother.

5. Does she often go to church, my boy Willie?
   Does she often go to church, Willie won't you tell me now?
   Yes, she often goes to church in a bonnet white as birch,
   But she is too young to be taken from her mother.

6. Can she make a feather-bed, my boy Willie?
   Can she make a feather-bed, Willie won't you tell me now?
   She can make a feather-bed, and put pillows at the head,
   But she is too young to be taken from her mother.

7. Did she ask you to come in, my boy Willie?
   Did she ask you to come in, Willie will you tell me now?
   Yes, she asked me to come in, she has a dimple in her chin,
   But she is too young to be taken from her mother.

8. Did she tell how old she is, my boy Willie?
   Did she tell how old she is, Willie won't you tell me now?
   She's three times six, seven times seven, twenty-eight and eleven,
   But she is too young to be taken from her mother.

# BILLY BOY

## (IRISH)

*The potato crop failure of 1840 in Ireland led to an immigration of many Irish, with their traditional songs, to the United States. Note that the Irish "Billy Boy" is very much like a jig tune.*

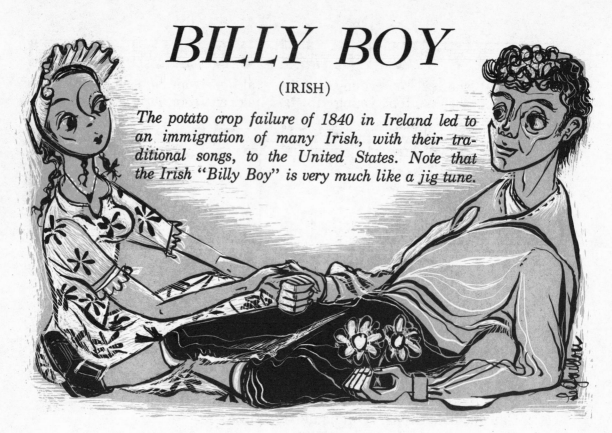

Bright, in 2

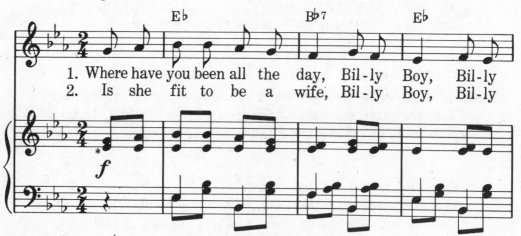

1. Where have you been all the day, Bil-ly Boy, Bil-ly
2. Is she fit to be a wife, Bil-ly Boy, Bil-ly

*The repeated E♭ in the right hand is optional.

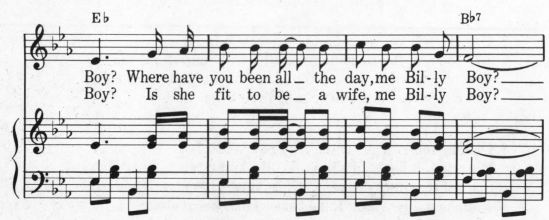

Boy? Where have you been all _ the day, me Bil-ly Boy? _
Boy? Is she fit to be _ a wife, me Bil-ly Boy? _

192.

I've been out with Nan-cy Gray, and she's
She's as fit to be a wife as a

stol-en me heart a-way.— She's me Nan-cy, tick-led me
fork fits to a knife.

fan-cy, oh, me charm-in' Bil-ly Boy.

193.

# THE DIVIL AND THE FARMER

*Of Irish and English origin, this version is from our midwest, where Irish immigrants worked on the railroads.*

**Easy - going, in 2**

1. A farm - er was plow - ing his field one day,
2. See here, me good man, I have come for your wife,

rite - ful, rite - ful, tit - ty - fie - day, a
rite - ful, rite - ful, tit - ty - fie - day, see

farm - er was plow - ing his field one day, when the
here, me good man, I have come for your wife,

div - il came up and to him he did say with a
she's the bane and tor - ment of your life, with a

rite - fa - la, tit - ty - fie - day,
rite - fa - la, tit - ty - fie - day,

rite - ful, rite - ful, tit - ty - fie - day.
rite - ful, rite - ful, tit - ty - fie - day.

3. When they got there the gates were shut,
   Riteful, riteful, titty fie day;
   When they got there the gates were shut,
   With a sweep of her hand she lay open his nut. *Chorus*

4. Two little divils were playing handball,
   Riteful, riteful, titty fie day;
   Two little divils were playing handball,
   They cried: "Take her out, daddy, she'll kill us all." *Chorus*

# THE DIVIL AND THE FARMER

5. So the divil he heisted her up on his hump,
   Riteful, riteful, titty fie day;
   So the divil he heisted her up on his hump,
   And back to earth with her he did jump.

   *Chorus*

6. "See here me good man, I have come with your wife,
   Riteful, riteful, titty fie day;
   See here me good man, I have come with your wife,
   She's the bane and torment of me life."

   *Chorus*

7. Oh they say that the women are worse than the men,
   Riteful, riteful, titty fie day;
   Oh they say that the women are worse than the men,
   They went down to hell and got chucked out again.

   *Chorus*

# AUNT RHODY

*Whether it began as a children's song or a play-party game, used in both ways, here is a song that is completely American in origin.*

Steady, in 2

Go  tell Aunt Rho-dy,  go  tell Aunt Rho-dy,

go  tell Aunt  Rho-dy  that her  old gray goose is

dead.____  The  one that she's been a - sav-in',  the

197.

# AUNT RHODY

cry - in', the gos - lings are cry - in', the gos - lings are

cry - in', 'cause their mam - my's dead. Go tell Aunt

Rho - dy,— go tell Aunt Rho - dy, go tell Aunt

Rho - dy that her old gray goose is dead.

*slower*

*l.h.*

199.

# THE WEE COOPER O'FIFE

*The early nineteenth century saw a great number of Scots coming over to join those who had come in 1745. They too brought their traditional songs.*

Gay, in 2

1. There was a wee coop-er wha lived i' Fife,
2. She would-na bake she would-na brew,

Nick - e - ty, nack - e - ty, noo, noo, noo, and
Nick - e - ty, nack - e - ty, noo, noo, noo, for

he ___ had got-ten a gen-tle wife,
spoil - ing of her come - ly hue,

Hey, Wil - lie Wal-lack - y, ho, John Dou - gal, a
Hey, Wil - lie Wal-lack - y, ho, John Dou - gal, a

lane quo rush - i - ty roo, ro, ro. ___
lane quo rush - i - ty roo, ro, ro. ___

3. She wouldna card, she wouldna spin,
   For the shamin' o' her gentle kin,

4. The cooper has gone to his woo' shack,
   And put a sheepskin across his wife's back,

5. I wouldna thrash for your gentle kin,
   But I would thrash my ain sheepskin,

6. Now ye what hae gotten a gentle wife,
   Just send ye for the wee cooper o' Fife,

# A BONNIE, WEE LASSIE

*Traditional: Scottish ballad.*
*Additional verse by MacKinlay Kantor.*

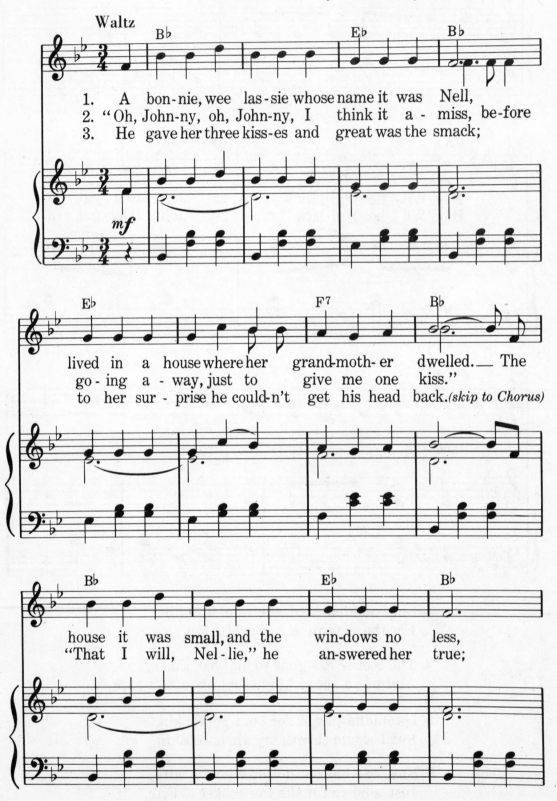

1. A bon-nie, wee las-sie whose name it was Nell,
2. "Oh, John-ny, oh, John-ny, I think it a - miss, be-fore
3. He gave her three kiss-es and great was the smack;

lived in a house where her grand-moth-er dwelled.— The
go - ing a - way, just to give me one kiss."
to her sur - prise he could-n't get his head back. *(skip to Chorus)*

house it was small, and the win-dows no less,
"That I will, Nel - lie," he an-swered her true;

hav-ing four panes, one need-ed a glass,— that
to her sur - prise— he poked his head through that
(3.) from that

nice lit-tle win-dow, the cute lit-tle win-dow, the
hole in the win-dow, that nice lit-tle win-dow, that
hole in the win-dow, that nice lit-tle win-dow, that

sweet lit - tle win-dow where grand-moth-er dwelled.
cute lit - tle win-dow where grand-moth-er dwelled.
cute lit - tle win-dow where grand-moth-er dwelled.

4. He ripped and he tore and he cursed and he swore,
Grandma heard the racket, jumped out on the floor;
She grabbed for the poker and a lick she gave one,
Another like that would have broke his backbone,
   With his head in the window, that nice little window, etc.

5. She lifted the ladle from out of the pot,
No batter e'er took the beating he got;
He ran down the road with might and with main,
While around his shoulder the sash and the frame
   Of that cute little window, that sweet little window, etc.

# OLD BLUE

*Traditional southern and midwestern United States.*

**In 2, but not too fast**

1. I had an old dog _____ and his name was
2.   Chased that 'pos-sum _____ up a 'sim-mon

Blue, _____ and I bet-cha five
tree; _____ Blue looked at the

dol-lars he's a good dog too, ____ say-in', "Come on,
'pos-sum,'pos-sum looked at me ____ say-in', "Go on,

Blue, _____ mm mm". ____
Blue, _____ you can have some too." ____

3. Baked that 'pos-sum, good and brown,
   Laid them sweet potatoes 'round and 'round,
   Saying, "Come on, Blue,
   You can have some too."

4. Old Blue died and he died so hard,
   That he jarred the ground in my backyard,
   Saying, "Go on, Blue,
   I'm a-comin' too."

5. I dug his grave with a silver spade,
   And I let him down with a golden chain,
   Saying, "Go on, Blue,
   I'm a-comin' too."

6. When I get to Heaven, first thing I'll do,
   Grab my horn, and I'll blow for OLD BLUE,
   Saying, "Come on, Blue,
   Fin'lly got here too."

# SOURWOOD MOUNTAIN

*Mountain fiddle tune, words traditional.*

**Steady, like a square dance**

1. Chick - en a - crow-ing on Sour-wood Moun-tain,
2. My true love is a blue - eyed dai - sy,
3. My true love lives at the head of the hol - ler,
4. Ducks in the pond, geese in the o - cean,

hoe dee-ing_ di did-dy - I - day;

So man-y pret-ty girls,
If I don't get_ her
Dev-il's in wom - an

I can't count 'em,
I'll go cra - zy, hoe dee-ing di did-dy - I - day.
I won't fol - ler,
if she takes the no-tion,

206.

The mountain areas have produced songs, both ballads and dance tune songs, which are among our most effective anonymous folk songs. "Sourwood Mountain," "Down in the Valley," "I'm Sad and I'm Lonely," and "Lolly Too Dum" are all mountain tunes.

# Down in the Valley

**Waltz, gentle**                    *Traditional mountain song.*

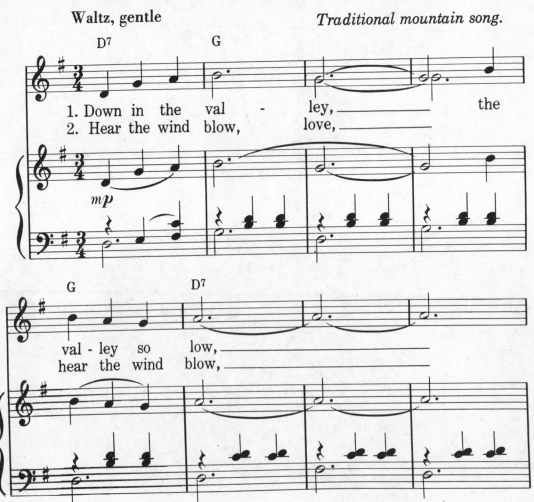

1. Down in the val - ley, _____ the
2. Hear the wind blow, love, _____

val - ley so low, _____
hear the wind blow, _____

hang your head   o  -  ver,_____
hang your head   o  -  ver,_____

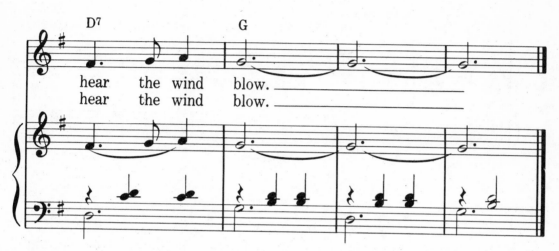

hear    the wind    blow._____
hear    the wind    blow._____

3. Roses love sunshine,
   Violets love dew,
   Angels in heaven
   Know I love you.

4. If you don't love me,
   Love who you please,
   Put your arms 'round me,
   Give my heart ease.

5. Give my heart ease, love,
   Give my heart ease,
   Put your arms 'round me,
   Give my heart ease.

6. Write me a letter,
   Send it by mail,
   Send it in care of
   The Birmingham Jail.

7. Birmingham Jail,
   Birmingham Jail,
   Send it in care of
   The Birmingham Jail.

8. Build me a castle
   Forty feet high,
   So I can see her
   As she rides by.

9. As she rides by, love,
   As she rides by,
   So I can see her,
   As she rides by.

10. Down in the valley,
    The valley so low,
    Hang your head over,
    Hear the wind blow.

209.

# LOLLY TOO DUM

*Traditional mountain dialogue song.*

Steady, in 2

1. As I went out one morn-in' to take the pleas-ant air, Lol-ly-too-dum, too-dum, lol-ly-too-dum-day; as I went out one
2. You bet-ter go wash them dish-es and hush that flat-ter-in' tongue, Lol-ly-too-dum, too-dum, lol-ly-too-dum-day; you bet-ter go wash them
3. "O pit-y my con - di-tion, just like you would your own," Lol-ly-too-dum, too-dum, lol-ly-too-dum-day; "O pit-y my con-

morn - in' to take the pleas - ant air, I
dish - es and hush that flat-ter-in' tongue, for you
di - tion, just like you would your own: for

o - ver - heard a moth - er a-scold-in' her daugh-ter
know that you want to git mar-ried, and that you are too
four - teen long years I've been liv - in' a-

fair, Lol-ly-too-dum, too-dum, lol-ly-too-dum-day.—
young, Lol-ly-too-dum, too-dum, lol-ly-too-dum-day.—
lone," Lol-ly-too-dum, too-dum, lol-ly-too-dum-day.—

4. "Supposin' I were willin' where would you git your man?
"Lawdy massy, mammy, I'd marry that handsome Sam,"

5. "Supposin' he should spite you like you done him before,
"Lawdy massy, mammy, I could marry forty more."

6. "They's peddlers and they's tinkers and boys from the flow,
Lawdy massy, mammy, I'm a-gitting that feeling now!"

7. "Now my daughter's married and well fer-to-do,
Gather around, young fellers, I'm on the market, too,"

211.

# I'm Sad
# and I'm Lonely

*Traditional "lonesome" tune.*

1. I'm sad\_\_\_\_ and\_\_ I'm lone-ly,\_\_\_\_
2. Young la-dies,\_\_\_\_ take\_\_ a warn-ing,\_\_\_\_

\_\_\_ my heart it will break, for my sweet-heart loves an -
\_\_\_ take a warn-ing from me: oh,\_\_ don't\_\_ waste your af -

oth -er; oh,\_\_\_\_ I wish I was dead.\_\_\_\_
fec - tions\_\_\_\_ on a young man so free.\_\_\_\_

3. Because he'll hug you and he'll
      kiss you
And he'll tell you more lies
Than the cross-ties on the railroad
Or the stars in the sky.

4. My cheeks once were red
Like the red, red rose;
But now they are white
As the lily that grows.

5. I'll build me a cabin
On the mountain so high,
Where the blackbirds can't find me
Or hear my sad cry.

6. I'm troubled, yes, I'm troubled,
I'm troubled in my mind,
If this trouble don't kill me,
I'll live a long time.

*Repeat Verse 1*

213.

# CARELESS LOVE

*Folk version of Negro, Ohio River packet-boat song.*

**Not too slow, in 2**

1. Love, oh, love, oh, care-less love. _____
( 2.) love my mam-my and my pap-py, too. _____ I

Love, oh, love, oh, care-less love. _____
love my mam-my and my pap-py, too. _____ I

214.

Love, oh, love, oh, care-less love, can't you
love my mam-my and my pap - py, too; gon - na

(a tempo)

(a tempo)

see, what love has done to me?_____ 2. I
leave 'em both and go with you._____

slower

slower

3. It's on this railroad bank I stand,
   On this railroad bank I stand,
   It's on this railroad bank I stand;
   I know I'm gonna kill a railroad man.

   *Chorus*

# Skip To My Lou

*Traditional play-party song.*

Bright, in 2

1. ____ Flies in the but-ter-milk, two by two,
2. If you can't get a red-bird, a blue-bird 'll do, if you

flies in the but-ter-milk, two by two,
can't get a red-bird, a blue-bird 'll do, if you

flies in the but-ter-milk, two by two,
can't get a red-bird, a blue-bird 'll do,

skip to my Lou, my dar' wup! She's gone a-gain, skip —

— to my Lou, she's gone a-gain, skip — to my Lou, she's

gone a-gain, skip — to my Lou, skip to my Lou, my dar-ling.

3. I've lost my girl, now what'll I do;

4. I'll get another, a better one too.

5. Pa's got a shotgun, Number 32—

6. Hurry up slowpoke, do, oh, do.

7. My girl wears a number nine shoe—

8. When I go courting, I take two.

9. Gone again, now what'll I do—

10. I'll get another one sweeter than you.

11. He's got big feet and awkward, too—

12. Kitten in the haymow, mew, mew, mew.

13. I'll get her back in spite of you.

14. We'll keep it up 'til half past two—

15. One old boot and a run-down shoe.

16. Stole my partner, skip to my Lou.

# TURKEY IN THE STRAW

*Folk Parody of 1834 hit "Old Zip Coon."*

In a gay dance tempo

1. As__ I was go-in'__ down the road, a__ tired team an' a heav-y load, I__crack'd my whip and the lead-er sprung and says,__ day-day, to the wag-on tongue.

2. Oh,__ I went out to milk, and I did-n't know how; I__ milked a goat in-stead of a cow. A__mon-key sit-tin' on a pile of straw, a - wink-in' his eye at his moth-er-in-law.

218.

CHORUS:

Tur-key in the straw, tur-key in the hay;
Tur-key in the hay, tur-key in the straw, the

dance_ all_ night and work_ all_ day;
old_ gray_ mare won't gee_ nor_ haw;

Roll 'em up and twist 'em up a - high, tuck - a - haw, and_

hit 'em up a tune_ call'd_ Tur-key in the Straw.

219.

3. Turkey in the hay, turkey in the straw;
   The old gray mare won't gee no haw;
   Roll 'em up and twist 'em up a high tuckahaw,
   And hit 'em up a tune call'd Turkey in the Straw.

   *Chorus*

4. Well, I met Mister Catfish com' down the stream;
   Says Mister Catfish, "What does you mean?"
   I caught Mister Catfish by the snout,
   And I turned Mister Catfish wrong side out.

   *Chorus*

5. Then I come to the river and I couldn't get across,
   So I paid five dollars for an old blind hoss.
   Well, he wouldn't go ahead, and he wouldn't stand still,
   So he went up and down like an old sawmill.

   *Chorus*

6. As I came down the new-cut road,
   I met Mister Bullfrog, I met Miss Toad,
   And every time Miss Toad would sing,
   The old Bullfrog cut a pigeon wing.

   *Chorus*

# GRANDFATHER'S CLOCK

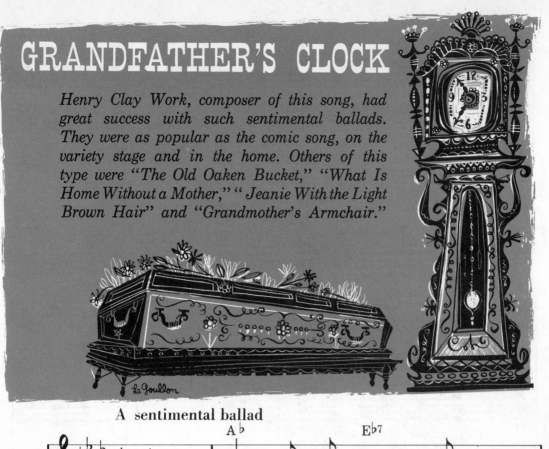

*Henry Clay Work, composer of this song, had great success with such sentimental ballads. They were as popular as the comic song, on the variety stage and in the home. Others of this type were "The Old Oaken Bucket," "What Is Home Without a Mother," "Jeanie With the Light Brown Hair" and "Grandmother's Armchair."*

A sentimental ballad

1. My grand - fa - ther's clock was too
it was tall - er by half than the
2. In watch - ing its pen - du - lum
and in child - hood and man - hood the

large for the shelf, so it stood nine - ty years on the floor;
old man him - self, tho it weighed not a pen - ny - weight more.
swing to and fro, man - y hours had he spent while a boy;
clock seem'd to know, and to share both his grief and his joy.

1. It was bought on the morn  of the day that he was born, and was
2. For it struck twen-ty-four when he  en-ter'd at the door with a

al - ways his treas-ure and   pride;        but it stopped short,
bloom-ing and beau-ti - ful    bride;

nev- er  to  go  a-gain, when the  old man   died.   Nine-ty

**CHORUS:**

years with-out slum-ber - ing:    tick,  tick,  tick,   tick, his

222.

life's sec-onds num-ber-ing: tick, tick, tick, tick, it stopped short,

nev-er to run a-gain, when the old man died.

*slower and slower till the end*

3. My grandfather said, that of those he could hire,
Not a servant so faithful he found;
For it wasted no time, and had but one desire—
At the close of each week to be wound,
And it kept in its place not a frown upon its face,
And its hands never hung by its side;
But it stopp'd, short, never to go again
When the old man died.

*Chorus*

# OLD DAN TUCKER

*Folk version of Dan Emmett's minstrel song.*

As fast as possible, but steady

1. Went to town the oth-er night to
2. Old Dan Tuck-er come to town

hear a noise and see a fight.
rid-ing a bil-ly goat, lead-ing a hound.—

All the peo-ple s was jump-in' a-round, and said,
Hound barked and the bil-ly goat jumped, and —

"Old Dan Tuck-er's a-com - in' to town.— Hey, get
throwed Dan Tuck-er right strad - dle of a stump.

CHORUS:

out - a the way for Old Dan Tuck-er!— Too late to

get his sup-per.— Sup-per's o - ver, din-ner's cook-in', Old

Dan Tuck-er just stand there look-in'.—

3. Old Dan Tucker, he got drunk,
   Jumped in the fire and he kicked up a hunk.
   He got a live coal in his shoe—
   Holy godermighty, how the ashes flew! *Chorus*

4. Old Dan Tucker is a fine old man,
   Washed his face in a frying pan,
   Combed his hair with a wagon wheel,
   Run away with a toothache in his heel. *Chorus*

# KEMO-KIMO

*This song was taught me by Uncle Mose, a Mississippi boatman, in his late eighties when I was five. It originates from a popular Negro dialect song about 1840.*

226.

CHORUS:

Ke mo, Ki mo, dear, ah ho, Ma hi, ma hon,

Wil - lie, Bil - lie, wink dum, rum - pa dum - pa doo dah,

milk bag sucked it, sing song, Pat-ty, won't you Ki me oh?

2. Milk in the dairy nine days old,
   Sing song Kitty, won't you ki me oh.
   Frogs and the skeeters getting mighty bold,
   Sing song Billy, won't you ki me oh.
   Frogs and the skeeters getting mighty bold,
   Sing song Patty, won't you ki me oh.
   Their legs hung out for the chickens to roost,
   Sing song Patty, won't you ki me oh.
   *Chorus*

227.

# The Blue-Tail Fly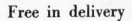

*Folk version of Dan Emmett's minstrel song.*

**Free in delivery**

1. When I was young I used to wait on my mas-ter and give him his plate, and pass the bot-tle when he got dry, and brush a-way the

2. And when he'd ride in the af-ter-noon, I'd fol-low af-ter with a hick-o-ry broom; the po-ny be-ing rath-er shy when bit-ten by a

3. One day he ride a-round the farm; the flies so nu-mer-ous they did swarm; one chanc'd to bite him in the thigh; the dev-il take the

228.

## CHORUS:

blue-tail fly. Jim-mie crack corn and I don't care,

Jim-mie crack corn and I don't care, Jim-mie crack corn and

I don't care, my mas-ter's gone a - way.

4. The pony run, he jump, he pitch,
   He threw my master in the ditch.
   He died, and the jury wondered why—
   The verdict was the blue-tail fly. *Chorus*

5. They lay him under a 'simmon tree;
   His epitaph is there to see:
   "Beneath this stone I'm forced to lie,
   A victim of the blue-tail fly." *Chorus*

229.

# BUFFALO GALS

*Based on the Negro dialect song, "Lubly Fan," 1844.*

**Bright, in 2**

1. Buf-fa-lo gals, won't you come out to-night, won't you come out to-night, won't you come out to-night, Buf-fa-lo gals, won't you come out to-night and dance by the light of the moon? Oh,

2. Wich-i-ta gals, ain't you com-in' out to-night, ain't you com-in' out to-night, ain't you com-in' out to-night, Wich-i-ta gals, ain't you com-in' out to-night and dance by the light of the moon? Oh,

CHORUS:

# THE ABOLITIONIST HYMN

*With rising feeling over the slavery issue, the New England churches began singing secular hymns against slavery much as they sang hymns against the British during the Revolution. This popular anti-slavery hymn was sung to the familiar melody of "Old Hundred."*

Definite, but not too slow

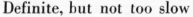

1. We ask not that the slave should lie as lies his
2. We ask not "eye for eye" that all who forge the
3. We mourn not that the man should toil: 'tis Na-ture's

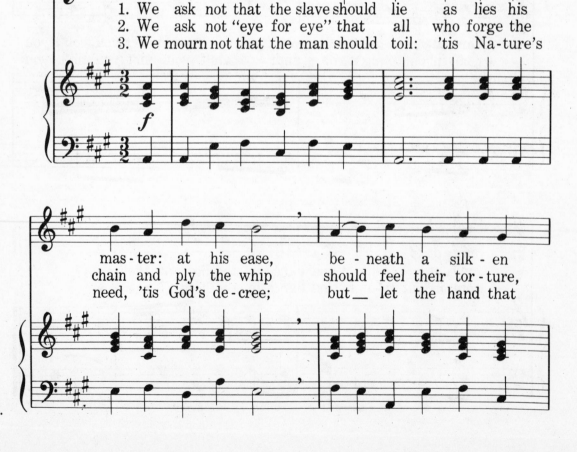

mas - ter: at his ease, be - neath a silk - en
chain and ply the whip should feel their tor - ture,
need, 'tis God's de - cree; but__ let the hand that

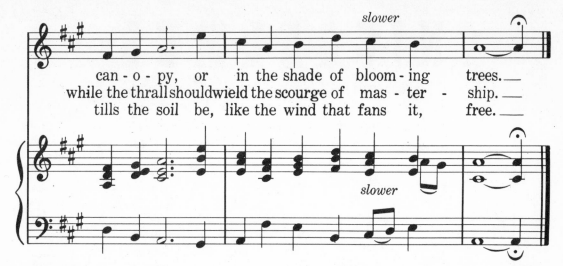

can - o - py,    or    in the shade of bloom - ing    trees.___
while the thrall should wield the scourge of mas - ter - ship.___
tills the soil  be,  like the wind that fans  it,    free.___

*The New England attitude toward slavery is well expressed by a conversation between the Englishman, James Fleet, and a Negro reaping wheat on Long Island in 1818: "You work very hard?" "No Sir, I can do much more in the time, but that is of no use." "You are not free, then?" "No Sir, I a slave, I 'longs to Jacob Van ——— there." "But you black people are very well treated here?" "Oh yes Sir, master very good to me, give me everything he eat self, but no Sunday clothes." "You may live happier than some poor free people?" "That may be true, Sir, but put a bird in a cage, give him plenty to eat, still he fly away."*

# NICODEMUS

*This folk version of Henry Clay Work's sentimental picture of a Negro slave is little changed from the original. It is in the same sympathetic tradition as Stephen Foster's "Old Uncle Ned."*

Very free in delivery, in 2

1. Nic - o - de - mus, the slave was of Af - ri - can
   he was reck - oned as part of the salt of the
2. Nic - o - de - mus was nev - er the sport of the
   There were none of his mas - ters so bold or so

*mf*

birth and was bought for a bag - ful of gold;___
earth, and he died long a - go, ver - y old.___
lash tho' the bul - lets had oft' cross'd his path.___
rash as to face such a man in his wrath.___

*slow*

Gentle, in 2

But his last sad re - quest, as they laid___ him to
But his great heart with kind - ness was filled___ to the

*mp*

234.

rest in the trunk of an old hol-low tree: _____ "Wake me
brim; he o-beyed who was born to com-mand, _____ and he

up," was his charge, "at the first break of day, wake me
longed for the morn - in' which then was so dim: 'tis the

up for the great Ju - bi - lee." _____ There's a
morn - in' which now is at hand. _____

slower
slower

CHORUS:    Like a square dance, in 2

great time com - in' and it's not far off; been

mf

235.

# NICODEMUS

long, long, long__ on the way. So go and tell 'Li - ge to

hur-ry up home and meet us by the gum tree down in the

swamp for to wake Nic - o - de - mus to - day.

# THE FRONTIERS OF AMERICA
## 1800-1850

History and social events come alive when documented with examples that reach down to the level of individual experience. What one immediately recognizes in a folk song is this basic immediacy of personal experience, which gives the song its strength. These songs relate as a personal experience, what on a larger scale can be regarded as a major historical trend or event. All of the songs that we have looked at in the previous chapters were sung during the period of America's growth and are a part of the life of that period.

As we saw in the first part of this book, when the Atlantic Coast was the American frontier it was the frontier of Europe and the songs were the songs of Europe with occasional new verses to fit a colonial event. During the Revolutionary period the American frontier crossed the Alleghenies into Kentucky, Tennessee, and the upper part of Ohio. This was our first "West." The songs of these people were the songs of the eastern seaboard which were the songs of England changed, perhaps, but basically the same.

After the Revolutionary War new settlers poured across the country and by 1820 the eastern bank of the Mississippi was the western frontier. Flatboats and eventually steamboats, canal boats, and railroads—all the modes of travel—had their history of development and their songs to tell about it.

After the War of 1812 a network of new canals and new roads greatly accelerated westward movement and connected the Atlantic with the midwestern rivers. The men along the rivers and the rest of the country sang about this new development. Variety hall canal songs were published, sung, and changed into the more easily remembered versions that developed by word of mouth and are to this day the folk songs of the Erie Canal.

Hardly had the canals proved their value than the railroads followed. In 1828 construction of the Baltimore and Ohio Railroad between Baltimore and St. Louis was started. The railroads experimented with sails and horses, but in 1829 the first steam locomotive was imported from Great Britain. The first railroad song, "The Railroad Chorus," was dedicated to the directors of the Baltimore and Ohio. A typical verse went:

> Singing through the forest,
> Rattling over ridges,
> Shooting under arches,

239

Running over bridges,
Whizzing through the mountains,
Buzzing o'er the vale,
Bless me! this is pleasant
A-riding on a rail.
Singing through the mountains,
Buzzing o'er the vale,
Bless me! this is pleasant
A-riding on a rail.

Beginning in 1821 great wagon trains were organized at Franklin or Independence on the Missouri River. These went down the Santa Fe trail. By permission of the Mexican Government, Americans were allowed to settle in the Mexican province of Texas. The wagoners who drove the oxen were a special group of men with their own professional ethics. At this period, too, the Lewis and Clark expedition opened up the Oregon Territory for settlement, preceded only by fishermen, fur traders, and miners. Settlers in the northward trek had to pass through the territory of the Sioux Indians, with whom they had many a fight. Popular songs like "Joe Bowers," parodies of popular songs like "Sweet Betsy," anonymous ballads like "Sioux Indians" and the "Ox-Driving Song," and many others told seriously and humorously about the pioneers and these aspects of their life.

Wars of Annexation—America fought for her new territories with the Florida Indians, with Indians across the country, and with the Mexicans. In 1814 General Jackson defeated the Creeks in Alabama and Tennessee. In 1819 he fought the Indians in Florida, where the remnants of the Creeks joined with the Seminoles, and were defeated. Soldiers of the Florida War had their own minstrel, Benjamin Beall, whose stories and songs had great success among the troops. One of his own men wrote about him:

Oh, a jolly brave knight was our Benjamin Beall
        In the Florida War;
As many a jolly bright camp-fire could tell
        In the Florida War.
Oh! the stories he told that never grow old
And the songs that he trolled until reveille rolled,
        In the Florida War,
Made Chiefs and subalterns as merry as bold.
        In the Florida War.

But we have no songs of Beall's own writing today.

In the middle 1830's Texas fought for freedom against Santa Anna, the Mexican dictator, and became an independent country. The memory of the brave stand of David Austin, David Crockett, and James Bowie, who fought for Texas Independence, was remembered in song:

When sounds the thrilling bugle blast,
And "Charge" from rank to rank is passed
Then, as your saber-strokes fall fast,
Remember the Alamo!

For every wound and every thrust
On prisoners dealt by hand accurst

A Mexican shall bite the dust.
Remember the Alamo!

The public sang about the legendary hero, David Crockett, to the tune of "The Star Spangled Banner" and a typical verse went:

He fought, but no valor that horde could withstand;
He fell—but behold where the wan victor found him!
With a smile on his lips, and his rifle in hand,
He lay with his foemen heaped redly around him;
   His heart poured its tide
   In the cause of his pride;
A freeman he lived and a freeman he died;
For Liberty struggled, for Liberty bled—
May his name and his fame to the last—Go ahead!

From the very beginning there was agitation in Texas and in Washington for annexation. However, it was not until 1845 that a war with Mexico was fought in order to insure Texas' position as a state in the Union. The feelings about acquisition ran high and there were many songs to stir up the public.

With the end of the Mexican War came the acquisition of California, and the Gold Rush of 1849, both of which inspired many songs. Crossing the plains to homestead or ranch, hastening to California in search of gold, the settlers fashioned songs to fit the events.

Medicine shows, minstrel shows, cheaply printed song collections (original songs or parodies) taught the settlers the music that was being written about them. The Negro slaves who accompanied the Southern wagon trains brought their plantation melodies, the New Englanders brought their hymns. Indian war chants, the gay refrains of the occasional French trader, camp meeting hymns, play-party dances and the popular music of the entertainment halls of the East constituted the music of the frontier. And these were the songs so diversely created, which give us insight into the attitudes and events of the American frontier as it went west.

241.

# The Young Man Who Wouldn't Hoe Corn

*On the frontier everybody worked; "the young man who wouldn't"*
*is a comic fiction. Benjamin Franklin wrote in 1775 that "Amer-*
*ica is the land of labor and by no means the English lubberland."*

Free in delivery

1. I'll sing you a song, and it's not ver-y long, a-
2. He went to the field, and he took a peep in: the

bout a young man who would-n't hoe corn. The
weeds and the grass was up to his chin, the

rea - son why, I can't tell, for
weeds and the grass, they were so high, they

this young man was al - ways well. _____
caused this young man for to sigh. _____

3. He went down to his neighbor's door
Where he had been many times before;
Pretty little miss, will you marry me,
Pretty little miss, what do you say?

4. Well, here you air a-wantin' for to wed
And cannot make your own corn bread.
Single I be, single I remain;
A lazy man I won't maintain.

5. Now go down to that cute little widder,
And I hope that you don't git her.
She gave him the mitten as sure as you're born,
Because this young man wouldn't hoe corn.

243.

# THE SOW TOOK THE MEASLES

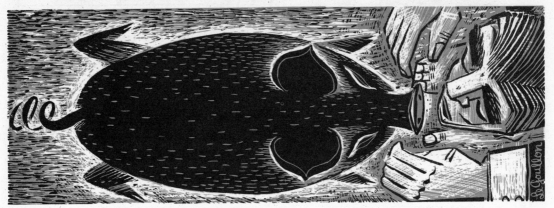

The resourcefulness of a frontier settler is humorously told in this song. William Cobbett reported in London in 1818: "Besides the great quantity of work performed by the American, his skill, *the* versatility *of* his talent, is a great thing. Every man can use an axe, a saw, and a hammer. Very few indeed, who cannot kill and dress pigs and sheep, and many of them oxen and calves. Every farmer is a neat butcher; a butcher for market; and, of course, the boys must learn. This is a great convenience. It makes you so independent as to a main part of the means of house keeping. All are ploughmen. In short, a good labourer here can do anything that is to be done upon a farm."

Free in delivery

CHORUS

How do you think I be-gan in the world? I got me a sow and sev-'ral oth-er things. The

sow took the mea-sles, and she died in the spring.

1. What do you think I made of her hide? The
2. What do you think I made of her nose? The
3. What do you think I made of her tail? The
4. What do you think I made of her feet? The

ver-y best saddle that you ev-er did ride.— Sad-dle or bri-dle or
ver-y best thimble that_ ev-er sewed clothes. Thimble or thread or
ver-y best whup that_ ev-er sought sail. Whup or whup-sock-et,
ver-y best pickles that you ev-er did eat.— Pick-les or glue or

an-y such thing, the sow took the measles, and she died in the spring.
an-y such thing, the sow took the measles, and she died in the spring.
an-y such thing, the sow took the measles, and she died in the spring.
an-y such thing, the sow took the measles, and she died in the spring.

# THE GREY GOOSE

*Tales of exaggeration, tall tales, were one of the basic elements of frontier humor. The miraculous goose like "Brer Rabbit" is a Negro plantation creation.*

Rather fast in 2

1. Last Sun-day morn-ing, Lord, Lord, Lord,
2. dad-dy went a - hunt-ing; Lord, Lord, Lord, oh, my

last Sun-day morn-ing, Lord, Lord, Lord. 2. Oh, my
dad-dy went a - hunt-ing, Lord, Lord, Lord.

3. He went hunting for the grey goose.
   He went hunting for the grey goose.

4. And he took along his shot-gun,
   Yes, he took along his shot-gun.

5. And along come a grey goose,
   Yes, along come a grey goose.

6. Well it's up to his shoulder,
   And he pulled back the hammer.

7. And the gun went a-booloo,
   Oh, the gun went a-booloo.

8. He was six weeks a-fallin',
   He was six weeks a-fallin'.

9. And they had a feather-pickin',
   Oh, your wife and my wife.

10. He was nine months a-cookin',
    He was nine months a-cookin'.

11. Then they put him on the table,
    Yes, they put him on the table.

12. And the knife couldn't cut him,
    No, the knife couldn't cut him.

13. And the fork couldn't stick him,
    No, the fork couldn't stick him.

14. And the saw couldn't cut him,
    He broke the saw's tooth out.

15. So they took him to the hogpen,
    And the hogs wouldn't eat him.

16. And the last time I see'd him,
    Oh, the last time I see'd him.

17. He was flying o'er the ocean
    He was flying o'er the ocean

18. With a long string of goslins,
    With a long string of goslins.

19. They was all going "Quink, quank,"
    They was all going "Quink, quank."

20. That's the story of the grey goose,
    That's the story of the grey goose.

# PETER GRAY

*Folk version of comic song current in the early 19th century.*

In 2

1. Once on a time there lived a man, his name was Pe-ter Gray, _____ he lived way down in that 'ere town called Penn-syl-van-i - a.

2. Now Pe-ter fell in love all with a nice _ young girl, _____ the first three let-ters of her name were Lu - cy An-nie Pearl.

248.

CHORUS:

Blow, ye winds of morn-ing, blow, ye winds, heig-

ho,_____ blow, ye winds of

morn-ing,— blow, blow, blow._____

3. Just as they were about to wed
   Her father did say no,
   And consequently she was sent
   Beyond the O-hi-o.

   *Chorus*

4. When Peter heard his love was lost,
   He knew not what to say,
   He'd half a mind to jump into
   The Susquehan-ni-a.

   *Chorus*

5. Now Peter went away out west
   To seek his for-ti-an,
   But he was caught and scalp-i-ed
   By a bloody Ind-i-an.

   *Chorus*

6. When Lucy heard of this bad news
   She knew not what to say.
   She wep' and wep' and wep-i-ed
   Her poor sweet life away.

   *Chorus*

# THE ERIE CANAL

*Sailors by courtesy only, the bargemen of the Erie Canal are described in this song. The job of guiding mules or horses along the tow path was more tedious than dangerous except for the rough frontier character of the life. The canal, finished in 1825, helped open up Illinois, Wisconsin, and Michigan.*

In 2 (steady rhythm)

1. We were for-ty miles from Al-ba-ny,— for-
2. Our cap-tain he— came up on deck with a

get it I nev-er shall! What a ter-ri-ble storm we
spy glass in his hand,— and the fog it was so

had one night on the E - ri - ee Ca - nal!
tarn-al'd thick that he could-n't spy the land. The

250.

E - ri - ee was a - ris - in', — the gin was a-gittin' low, —

— and I scarce-ly think we'll git a drink — till we

git to Buf-fa - lo, — till we git to Buf-fa-lo. —

3. Our cook she was a grand ol' gal,
   She had a ragged dress.
   We hoisted her upon a pole
   As a signal of distress.

   *Chorus*

4. The captain he got married,
   And the cook she went to jail,
   And I'm the only son-of-a-gun
   That's left to tell the tale.

   *Chorus*

251.

# THE PRATIES THEY GROW SMALL

*Crop failure was the cause of the tremendous influx of Irishmen who came over in such large numbers in the early nineteenth century. A popular song of 1844 told about the small potato crop and landlord trouble in Ireland. Because this song touched the heart of a problem we find it preserved in the memory of many Irish families.*

Slow and sad

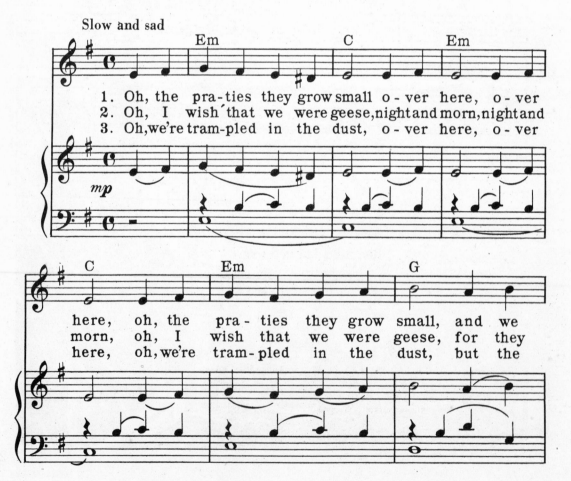

1. Oh, the pra-ties they grow small o-ver here, o-ver here, oh, the pra-ties they grow small, and we
2. Oh, I wish that we were geese, night and morn, night and morn, oh, I wish that we were geese, for they
3. Oh, we're tram-pled in the dust, o-ver here, o-ver here, oh, we're tram-pled in the dust, but the

Am       Bm       Em

dig them in the fall, and we eat them coats and
fly and take their ease, and they live and die in
Lord in whom we trust will give us crumb for

C       Am       Em

all,    o - ver    here,    o - ver    here.
peace   eat - in'   corn,    eat - in'   corn.
crust,    o - ver    here,    o - ver    here.

*(repeat first verse softly)*

253.

# Patrick on the Railroad

*Songs about "Patrick," the typical Irishman, were frequent as folk songs and on the Variety stage. The Irish, who did much of the labor on our first railroads, worked together in large groups and amused themselves by conversation, songs, the pun, and the bull.*

Easygoing, in 2

1. In eigh- teen hun- dred and for- ty- one, I put my cor- d'roy breech- es on, put my cor- d'roy breech- es on to work up- on the rail - way.
2. In eigh- teen hun- dred and for- ty-two, I left the ould world for the new, bad 'cess to the luck that brought me through to work up- on the rail - way.

**CHORUS:**

Bil - ly me - oo, re - eye, re - aye,
Bil - ly me - oo, re - eye, re - aye, Bil - ly me - oo, re -
eye, re - aye, to work up - on the rail - way.

3. Our boss's name it was Tom King,
    He kept a store to rob the men,
    A Yankee clerk with ink and pen,
    To cheat Pat on the railway.

4. It's "Pat do this," and "Pat do that,"
    Without a stocking or cravat,
    Nothing but an old straw hat,
    And Pat worked on the railway.

# Sweet Betsy From Pike

*Here is a humorous parody from Put's Golden Songster of a Variety Hall hit of the 1840's, "Villikins and his Dinah." For all its fun, it shows the difficulties and privations faced by the pioneers every day.*

Waltz

1. Do you re-mem-ber sweet Bet-sy from Pike?_
2. soon reached the des-ert where Bet-sy give out, _

'Crossed the big moun-tains with her lov-er Ike,_ with
down on the sand she lay roll-ing a bout._

two yoke of ox-en, a big yal-ler dog, a
Ike, he gazed at her with sobs and with sighs, quoth

tall Shang-hai roost-er, and one spot-ted hog._ Hoo-dle-
he,"Get up, Bet-sy, you'll get sand in your eyes."

CHORUS:

dang, fol - de - di - do, hoo-dle-dang, fol-de-day._ 2.They

3. The Shanghai ran off, and the cattle all died,
   The last piece of bacon that morning was fried.
   Ike got discouraged and Betsy got mad,
   The dog wagged his tail and looked wonderfully sad.

   *Chorus*

4. Long Ike and Sweet Betsy attended a dance;
   Ike wore a pair of his Pike County pants;
   Sweet Betsy was dressed up in ribbons and rings;
   Quoth Ike, "You're an angel, but where are your wings?"

   *Chorus*

5. A miner come up, says, "Will you dance with me?"
   "I will, you old hoss, if you don't make too free,
   And I'll tell you the reason, do you want to know why?
   Dawgone you, I'm chuckful of strong alkali."

   *Chorus*

257.

# YANKEE DOODLE
## (1845)

*"Yankee Doodle" again, and this time describing the annexation of Texas, and President Polk's stand on the Oregon Territory . . ."54-40 or Fight." This "Yankee Doodle" was found in a famous frontier volume of the time, The Rough and Ready Songster.*

*By this time the Americans were known to the British as "Yankees" or "Yankee Doodles." Mrs. Frances Trollope, early observer of American manners, wrote in 1831 of meeting an American who, "showed me, past contradiction, that the whole of the British dominions do not equal in size, one of their least important states; . . . after the demonstrations he placed his feet upon the chimney-piece, considerably higher than his head, and whistled 'Yankee Doodle'." Mrs. Trollope said she found the "Yankees" "ill-mannered, crude, money-grubbing, and boastful."*

1. Walk in my tall-haired Indian gal,
   Your hand, my star-eyed Texas;
   You're welcome to our
       White House hall,
   Though Mexy's hounds would
       vex us;

2. Come on and take some
       Johnny-cake,
   With 'lasses snug and coodle,
   For that and Independence make
   A full-blood Yankee Doodle.

   *Chorus:*
   Yankee Doodle is the word,
   Surpassing all creation,
   With the pipe or with the sword,
   It makes us love our nation.

3. My overseer, young Jimmy Polk,
   Shall show you all my nieces,
   And then the calumet we'll smoke
   Until our eagle sneezes;

4. If Johnny Bull's fat greedy boys
   About our union grumble,
   I'll kick up such a tarnal noise
   'Twill make 'em feel quite humble.

   *Chorus*

5. If Mexy, backed by secret foes,
   Still talks of taking you, gal,
   Why, we can lick 'em all, you know,
   And then annex 'em too, gal;

6. For Freedom's great millennium
   Is working airth's salvation,
   Her sassy kingdom soon will come,
   Annexin' all creation.

   *Chorus*

# You Who Don't Believe It

## (Air—"The Blue-Tail Fly")

*The two famous pocket songbooks of the "Forty-niners" were* Put's Original California Song-ster *and* Put's Golden Songster. *Whether Put collected these songs or composed them, they contained descriptive verses about the life of the Gold Rush, to be sung to well-known tunes.*

1. There is no land upon the earth,
   Contains the same amount
      of worth;
   And he that could not here reside,
   Had ought to freeze the other side!

   *Chorus:*
      You who don't believe it,
      You who don't believe it,
      You who don't believe it,
      Come yourselves and see!

2. We've got more gold than all
      the world,
   A flag that wins whene'er unfurled,
   And smarter men to help us
      through,
   Than England, France or Mexico.

   *Chorus*

3. We've smarter ships than
      Johnny Bull,
   Larger sheep with finer wool;
   A prison too! you cannot fail
   To throw a Bull through by the tail.

   *Chorus*

4. We raise the largest cabbage heads,
   Got more and better feather beds;
   Of everything we've got the best,
   And thieves until you cannot rest.

   *Chorus*

5. All ruffianism now is o'er,
   The country's safer than before;
   Our cities keep the rowdies straight,
   Or send them through the
      Golden Gate.

   *Chorus*

6. We've got the highest mountains
      here,
   Taller trees and faster deer,
   And travel more, at higher rates,
   Than people in the Eastern States.

   *Chorus*

7. We've got the smartest river boats,
   And, ten to one, old whiskey bloats;
   We're blest with very heavy fogs,
   And any amount of poodle dogs!

   *Chorus*

8. We've got a few unmarried g'hals,
   Railroads, ditches and canals;
   Although we did repudiate,
   A joke 'twas only to create.

   *Chorus*

9. To one and all, both young
      and old,
   You're welcome to the land of gold;
   So come along, be not afraid,
   We guarantee you all well paid!

   *Chorus*

259.

# THE OX-DRIVING SONG

*Ox teams going west from the Mississippi faced many odds: Indians, washouts, and bad muddy roads.*

Lively, in 2

1. Pop my whip and I bring the blood, I make my leaders
(2.) fourteenth day of Oc-to-ber-o   I hitched my team in
3. When I got there, the hills were steep; 'twould make any tenderhearted
(4.) I get home I'll __ have re-venge, I'll land my fam-i-ly a-

take the mud, we grab the wheels__ and we turn them a-
or-der-o   to drive the hills __ of Sa-lu-di-
per-son weep   to hear me cuss __ and pop my
mong my friends, I'll bid a-dieu __ to the whip and

round,   one long, long pull, and we're on hard ground.
o     to me roll, to me roll, to my ri-de-o.     To me
whip   and see my ox-en __ pull and slip.
line   and drive no more in the win-ter-time.

CHORUS:

261.

# JOE BOWERS

*This popular Gold Rush song reflects the constant dread of the men who were so long out of communication with their eastern homes: that those left behind might be dead or married to another before they could return.*

Lively, but free in delivery

1. My name it is Joe Bow-ers, and I've got a broth-er
2. I used to court a gal there; her_ name was Sal-lie

Ike; I'm just here from old Mis - sou - ri, and
Black; I asked her if she'd mar-ry me, she

all the way from Pike; I tell you why I
said it was a whack; says she to me, "Joe

left there and why I be-gan to roam, and
Bow-ers, be-fore we're hitched for life, you

left my ag-ed par-ents, so far a-way from home.
ought to get a lit-tle home to keep your lit-tle wife."

3. Says I, "My dearest Sally,
   O Sally, for your sake,
   I'll go to California
   And try to raise a stake."
   Says she to me, "Joe Bowers,
   You are the one to win."
   She gave me a kiss to seal
       the bargain—
   And I throwed a dozen in.

4. I'll never forget my feelings
   When I bid adieu to all.
   Sal, she cotched me round the neck
   And I began to bawl.
   When I began they all commenced,
   You never heard the like,
   How they all took on and cried
       and cried
   The day I left old Pike.

5. When I got to this country,
   I had nary a red,
   I had such wolfish feelings,
   That I wished myself most dead.
   But the thoughts of my dear Sally
   Soon made this feeling git:
   And whispered hopes to Bowers,
   Lord I wish I had 'em yit.

6. At last I went to mining,
   Put in my biggest licks,
   Come down upon the boulders
   Just like a thousand bricks.
   I worked both late and early
   In rain and sun and snow,
   I was working for my Sally,
   It was all the same to Joe.

# JOE BOWERS

7. One day I got a letter
From my dear brother Ike;
It came from old Missouri
All the way from Pike.
It brought me the darnedest news
That ever you did hear;
My heart it is a-breaking
So please excuse this tear.

8. It said my Sal was false to me,
That her love for me had fled,
That she got married to a butcher,
And the butcher's hair was red.
It told me more than that,
It's enough to make me swear
That Sally had a baby and
The baby had red hair.

9. Now I've told you everything
About this sad affair,
'Bout Sally marrying a butcher
And the baby had red hair.
But whether it was a boy or girl,
The letter never said,
It only said the baby's hair
Was inclinéd to be red.

# What Was Your Name in the States?

*It became the custom in America never to press questions on a stranger unless he himself volunteered information. There was a feeling of room for all in the new country, and of judging a man for what he was, regardless of his past. Thomas Cooper wrote in his Letters from America, 1795: "In America a false step is not irretrievable, there is room to get up again; and the less unfortunate stumbler looks round at leisure, and without dismay, for some profitable path to be pursued."*

What was your name in the States?__ Was it

Thomp-son or John-son or Bates?__ Did you

mur-der your wife and fly for your life? Say,

what was your name in the States?

# THE SIOUX INDIANS

*This song is a realistic ballad about the fight of a wagon train with the Sioux Indians, en route to Oregon territory, opened up by the Lewis and Clark Expedition. It is a non-melodic song to be chanted rather than sung. Traditionally it is sung unaccompanied.*

Free in delivery

1. I'll sing you a song, though it may be a sad one, of
2. I crossed the Mis-sour-i and joined a large train which

trials_ and trou-bles, and where first be- gun. I
bore us o'er moun-tain and val - ley and plain; and

left my dear kin-dred, my friends, and my home, and we
of-ten of eve-nings out hunt - ing we'd go to

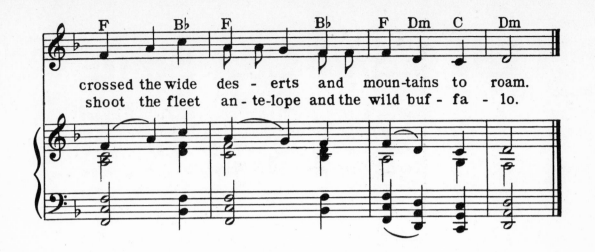

crossed the wide des - erts and moun-tains to roam.
shoot the fleet an - te-lope and the wild buf - fa - lo.

3. Without any money provisions to buy
   We'd sneak 'round the hills shooting elk on the sly;
   We'd shoot the fat deer and take him to town
   To buy flour to bake bread, and tea, a few pound.

   4. We heard of Sioux Indians, all out on the plains
      A-killin' poor drivers and burning their trains—
      A-killin' poor drivers with arrows and bow,
      When captured by Indians no mercy they'd show.

5. We traveled three weeks till we came to the Platte,
   And pitched out our tents at the head of a flat;
   We'd spread down our blankets on the green grassy ground,
   While our horses and oxen were a-grazing around.

   6. While taking refreshments we heard a low yell,
      The whoop of Sioux Indians coming up from the dell;
      We sprang to our rifles with a flash in each eye.
      "Boys," says our brave leader, "we'll fight till we die."

7. We gathered our horses, got ready to fight,
   As the band of Sioux Indians just came into sight.
   They came down upon us with a whoop and a yell,
   At the crack of our rifles oh six of them fell.

   8. They made a bold dash and came near to our train,
      And the arrows fell down just like hail and like rain,
      But with our long rifles we fed them cold lead
      'Til many a brave warrior around us lay dead.

9. With our small band, there were just twenty-four,
   And of the Sioux Indians there were five hundred or more,
   We fought them with courage, we spoke not a word,
   'Til the end of the battle that was all that was heard.

   10. We shot their bold Chief at the head of the band,
       He died like a warrior with the gun in his hand,
       When they saw their full Chief laying dead in his gore,
       They whooped and they yelled and we saw them no more.

11. We hitched up our horses and started our train,
    Three more bloody battles this trip on the plain.
    And in our last battle three of our brave boys they did fall,
    And we left them to rest in a green shady dell.

    12. We traveled by day, guarded camp during night,
        Till Oregon's mountains look'd high in their might
        Now at Pocahontas beside a clear stream
        Our journey has ended in the land of our dream.

# The Hand-Cart Song

*Conflicts with other settlers forced the Mormons west through heat and snow to the desolate Salt Lake valley, chosen by their ten leaders as the Promised Land. Here they laid out their famous city.*

Like a hymn (in 2)

1. Ye saints who dwell on Eu-rope's shore, pre-
Chorus: For some must push and some must pull as
2. For you must cross the rag-ing main be-

pare your-selves for man-y more,— to leave be-hind your
we go march-ing up— the hill, so mer-ri-ly on our
fore the prom-ised land— you gain, and with the faith-ful

na-tive land, for sure, God's judg-ments are at hand.
way we go, un-til we reach the val-ley, oh!
make a start to cross the plains with your hand-cart.

268.

3. The lands that boast of
     modern light,
We know are all as dark as night,
Where poor men toil and want
     for bread,
Where peasant hosts are blindly led.

4. These lands that boast of liberty,
You ne'er again would wish to see,
When you from Europe make a start
To cross the plains with
     your hand cart.
     *Chorus*

5. As on the road the carts are pulled,
'Twould very much surprise
     the world,
To see the old and feeble dame
Thus lend a hand to pull the same.

6. And maidens fair will dance
     and sing,
Young men as happy as a king.
And children too will laugh and play,
Their strength increasing day
     by day.
     *Chorus*

7. But some will say it is too bad
The saints upon the foot to pad.
And more than that to pull a load,
As they go marching o'er the road.

8. But then we say it is the plan,
To gather up the best of men,
And women too, for none but they
Will ever travel in this way.
     *Chorus*

9. And long before the valley's
     gained,
We will be met upon the plains,
With music sweet and friends
     so dear,
And fresh supplies our hearts
     to cheer.

10. And then with music and with
     song,
How cheerfully we'll march along,
And thank the day we made a start
To cross the plains with
     our hand cart.
     *Chorus*

11. When you get there among
     the rest,
Obedient be and you'll be blest,
And in God's chambers be shut in
With judgments cleanse the
     earth from sin.

12. For we do know it will be so,
God's servants spoke it long ago,
We say it is high time to start
To cross the plains with
     our hand cart.
     *Chorus*

Put's California Songster *looked at the Mormons with different eyes and the "Forty-niners" sang a fifteen-verse song that the Mormons themselves remember for us with tolerant amusement:*

> *"Brigham Young was a Mormon bold,*
> *And a leader of the roaring rams,*
> *And a shepherd of a heap of pretty little sheep,*
> *And a nice fold of pretty little lambs,*
> *And he lived with his five and forty wives,*
> *In the city of the Great Salt Lake*
> *Where they woo and coo as pretty doves do,*
> *And cackle like ducks to a drake."*

# Old Rosin the Beau

*One of the most popular songs of 1838—along with "Flow Gently Sweet Afton," "Annie Laurie," and "The West Pointer's Song"—"Old Rosin" is a prototype of songs about drinkers who attain popularity just before death. Words and music are anonymous.*

Like a waltz

1. I live for the good of my na - tion, ___ and my sons are all grow-ing low, but I hope that my next gen - er - a - tion will re - sem - ble old

2. In the gay round of pleas-ure I've trav - el'd, ___ nor will I be-hind leave a foe; and when my com-pan-ions are jo-vial, they will drink to old

Ros-in, the beau.___ I've trav-el'd this coun-try all
Ros-in, the beau.___ But my life is now drawn to a

o-ver, and now to the next I will go;
clos-ing, and all will at last_ be so:

for I know that good quar-ters a-wait me,___
so we'll take a full bump-er at part-ing,___

_ to wel-come old Ros-in, the beau.___
_ to the name of old Ros-in, the beau.___

*8va....*

271.

# ACRES OF CLAMS

*This is one of several parodies of "Old Rosin the Beau."*

1. No longer the slave of ambition,
I laugh at the world and its shams,
As I think of my pleasant condition,
Surrounded by acres of clams.

    *Chorus:*
    Surrounded by acres of
        cla-a-a-ms,
    Surrounded by acres of clams,
    As I think of my happy condition,
    Surrounded by acres of clams.

2. For each man who got rich
        by mining,
Perceiving that hundreds grew poor,
I made up my mind to try farming,
The only pursuit that was sure.

    *Chorus*

3. So, rolling my grub in my blanket,
I left all my tools on the ground,
I started one morning to shank it
For the country they call
        Puget Sound

    *Chorus*

4. Arriving flat broke in midwinter,
I found it enveloped in fog,
And covered all over with timber,
Thick as hair on the back of a dog.

272. *Chorus*

5. When I looked on the prospects
        so gloomy,
The tears trickled over my face,
And I thought that my travels had
        brought me,
To the end of the jumping off place.

    *Chorus*

6. I staked me a claim in the forest
And sat myself down to hard toil,
For two years I chopped and
        I worked it,
But I never got down to the soil.

    *Chorus*

7. I tried to get out of the country,
But poverty forced me to stay,
Until I became an old settler,
Then nothing could drive me away.

    *Chorus*

8. No longer the slave of ambition,
I laugh at the world and its shams,
As I think of my pleasant condition,
Surrounded by acres of clams.

    *Chorus*

# A Ripping Trip

*Those who could do so went to California by boat, although the trip around the Horn was uncomfortable and dangerous. After news of the Gold Rush, passage to the west became very difficult to get. This description of a voyage to San Francisco was a parody to the country dance tune, "Pop Goes the Weasel."*

1. You go aboard of a leaky boat,
And sail for San Francisco;
You've got to pump to keep
     her afloat,
You have *that*, by jingo.
The engine soon begins to squeak,
But nary thing to oil her;
Impossible to stop the leak—
     Rip goes the boiler!

2. The captain on the promenade,
Looking very savage;
Steward and the cabin maid
Fighting 'bout a cabbage;
All about the cabin floor,
Passengers lie seasick;
Steamer's bound to go ashore,
     Rip goes the physic!

3. "Pork and beans" they
     can't afford
To second cabin passengers;
The cook has tumbled overboard
With forty pounds of sassengers!
The engineer, a little tight,
Bragging on the Mail line,
Finally gets into a fight,
     Rip goes the engine!

4. The cholera begins to rage,
A few have got the scurvy;
Chickens dying in their cage,
Steerage topsy-turvy.
When you get to Panama,
Greasers want a back-load;
Officers begin to jaw,
     Rip goes the railroad!

5. When home, you'll tell an
     awful tale,
And always will be thinking
How long you had to pump and bail,
To keep the tub from sinking.
Of course you'll take a glass of gin,
'Twill make you feel so funny;
Some city sharp will rope you in,
     Rip goes your money!

# BEN BOLT

*"Ben Bolt" is a famous example of the new sentimental type of song that became so popular after the 1830's. Like most songs that gained wide currency, it has its quota of parodies.*

273.

# BEN BOLT

Free in delivery

1. Oh, don't you re-mem-ber sweet Al-ice, Ben Bolt, sweet
2. Oh, don't you re-mem-ber the school, Ben Bolt, and the

Al- ice, with hair__ so brown? She wept with de-light when you
mas-ter so kind and so true,__ and the lit- tle nook by the

gave her a smile, and trem-bled with fear__ at your
clear run- ning brook, where we gath-ered the flow-ers as they

frown. In the old church-yard in the val-ley, Ben Bolt, in a
grew? On the mas-ter's grave grows the grass, Ben Bolt, and the

cor-ner ob-scure and a-lone, they have fit-ted a slab of\
run-ning lit-tle brook is now dry, and of all the friends who were

gran-ite so grey, and sweet Al-ice lies un-der the\
school-mates then, there re-main, Ben, but you and

stone, they have fit-ted a slab of gran-ite so grey, and sweet\
I, and of all the friends who were school-mates then, there re-

Al-ice lies un-der the stone.\
main, Ben, but you and I.

# THE SHADY OLD CAMP

*This description of a ghost town appeared in* Put's
Golden Songster, *sung to the melody of "Ben Bolt."*

1. Oh don't you remember the shady old camp,
   That stood by the side of the brook,
   Where we lay on the ground after many a tramp,
   And the fireplace where we used to cook?
   The shady old camp has gone to decay,
   And the ham bone has dropped from the pin;
   The roof and the door both have rotted away,
   And the chimney has all tumbled in.

2. Oh, don't you remember the cool summer breeze,
   So welcome in June and July,
   And the table that stood 'neath the shady oak trees,
   At the foot of the mountain so high?
   The table is standing, as when we were there,
   Though not as we often have seen,
   For bushes have grown o'er the ground then so bare,
   And miners have worked our ravine!

3. Oh, don't you remember the mountains of snow,
   In sight from the camp all the year,
   And the valleys so green, where the wild flowers grow,
   And where we went hunting the deer?
   The cool little brook where we used to drink,
   Will always be running the same
   As when we were talking of home on the brink,
   Or cursing the day that we came.

4. Oh, don't you remember the well-beaten trail
   That led from the camp to the spring,
   And the potpies we made of the squirrel and quail,
   And the evenings when we used to sing?
   The trail and the spring we shall see them no more,
   Though never forget till we die;
   The shady old camp, with the ground for a floor,
   Forever, we bid thee good-by!

# THE LITTLE OLD SOD SHANTY

*The labors of the pioneer who staked a claim and tried to build a home were little sung. Peek's Guide to the West, 1837, said: "First comes the pioneer who depends for subsistence . . . upon the natural growth of vegetation and the proceeds of hunting . . . He builds his cabin, gathers around him a few families of similar taste . . . till the neighbors crowd around and he lacks elbow room. He disposes of cabin and corn field to the next class of emigrants and 'breaks for the high timber' . . . The next class of emigrants purchase the lands . . . and exhibit the picture and forms of plain, frugal, civilized life . . . The men of capital come."*

277.

# THE LITTLE OLD SOD SHANTY

**Steady, in 2**

1. I'm look-ing rath-er seed-y now while hold-ing down my
2. I rath-er like the nov-el-ty of liv-ing in this

claim; my vit-tles are not al-ways of the best,___ and the
way, though my bill of fare is-n't al-ways of the best,___ but I'm

mice play shy-ly round me as I nes-tle down to rest in my
hap-py as a clam on the land of Un-cle Sam in my

lit-tle old_sod shan-ty on the plain.___
lit-tle old_sod shan-ty in the west.___ Oh, the

278.

CHORUS:

hing-es are of leath-er and the win-dows have no glass, the boards, they let the howl-ing bliz-zard in. ____ You can see the hun-gry coy-ote, as he sneaks up through the grass to my lit-tle old _ sod shan-ty on the claim. ____

279.

# I've Got No Use For Women

*As in the parable of the fox and the grapes, since there were too few women in the west to go around songs grew up deriding them. Perhaps the camp followers of the Gold Rush inspired these bitter strains.*

Waltz (steady rhythm)

1. I've got no use for wom-en,_____ A
(2.) pal was a straight young cow-punch-er,_____

true one may nev-er be found,____ they'll stick by a
hon-est and up-right and square,____ but he turned to a

man for his mon-ey;_____ when it's gone they'll turn him
gam-bler and gun-man,____ and a wom-an sent him

down. _____ They're all a - like at the bot-tom: \_\_\_\_\_
there. _____ Quick-er and sur - er his gun-play \_\_\_\_\_

self- ish and grasp-ing for all. \_\_\_\_\_ They'll
till his heart and his bod - y lay dead: \_\_\_\_\_ when a

stick by a man when he's win-ning, \_\_\_\_\_ and
van- quil in - sult - ed her pic-ture, \_\_\_\_\_ he

laugh in his face when he falls. \_\_\_\_\_ My \_\_\_
filled him full \_ of lead. \_\_\_ My \_\_\_

281.

3. All night long they trailed him
Thru mesquite and chaparral
And I couldn't but think of
    that woman,
As I saw him pitch and fall.
If she'd been the pal that she
    should have,
He might have been raising a son,
Instead of out there on the prairie
To fall by a ranger's gun.

4. Death's slow sting did not
    trouble—
His chances for life were too slim—
But where they were a-puttin'
    his body
Was all that worried him.
He lifted his head on his elbow,
The blood from his wound flowed red;
He looked at his pals grouped
    around him
And whispered to them, and said:

5. "Oh, bury me out on the prairie
Where the coyotes may howl o'er
    my grave,
Bury me out on the prairie,
And some of my bones please save.
Wrap me up in my blanket
And cover me deep 'neath the ground,
Cover me over with boulders
Of granite huge and round."

6. So they buried him out on
    the prairie,
And the coyotes still howl o'er
    his grave,
But his soul is now a-restin'
From the unkind cut she gave.
And many a sim-u-lar cowpuncher,
As he rides by that pile of stones,
Recalls some sim-u-lar woman
And envies his moldin' bones.

# When I Was Single

*For this extension of the anti-feminine viewpoint of the preceding song, the less comment the better.*

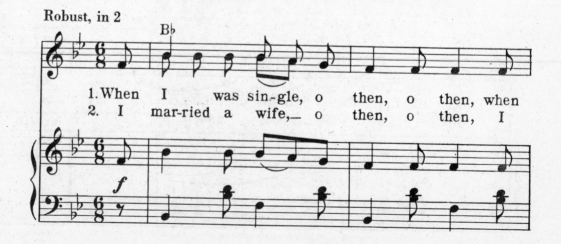

Robust, in 2

1. When I was sin-gle, o then, o then, when
2. I mar-ried a wife,— o then, o then, I

I was sin-gle, o then, — when I was sin-gle my
mar-ried a wife, o then, — I mar-ried a wife, she's the

mo-ney did jin-gle, and I wish I was sin-gle a-
curse of my life, I wish I was sin-gle a-

gain, a-gain, wish I was sin-gle a - gain. —
gain, a-gain, wish I was sin-gle a - gain. —

3. My wife she died, oh then, oh then,
   My wife she died, oh then,
   My wife she died and I laughed 'til I cried
   To think I was single again, again,
   To think I was single again.

4. I married me another, oh then, oh then,
   I married me another, oh then,
   I married me another, she's the devil's stepmother
   And I wish I was single again, again,
   I wish I was single again.

# POOR BOY

*Of Negro origin, probably of a later period, this song deserves a place here because one is apt to forget that a personal and intensive life with its own code was lived on the frontier and the river settlements.*

Steady waltz rhythm

1. As I went down to the riv-er, poor boy, to see the ships go by, ____ my sweet-heart stood on the deck of one, ____ and
2. I fel-lered her for months and months, she of-fered me her hand, ____ we were just a-bout ____ to get mar-ried, when ____ she
3. He come at me with a big jack knife; I went at him with lead. ____ When the fight ____ was o-ver, ____ poor boy, he

she waved        to me good-bye._____
ran off with a gam - blin' man._____        Bow down your
lay down be-side me,_____ dead._____

head and cry, poor boy,        bow down your head and

cry._____        Stop think-ing a - bout _ that wom-an you love,_

_ bow down your head and        cry._____

285.

4. They took me to the big jail house;
   The months, the months rolled by.
   The jury found me guilty, poor boy,
   And the judge said, you must die.

   *Chorus*

5. And yet they call this justice, poor boy,
   Then justice let it be.
   I only killed a man that was
   Just a-fixing to kill me.

   *Chorus*

# THE UTAH IRON HORSE

*The Mormons, in whose city of Salt Lake the two parts of the Union Pacific Railroad met, sang this song about its coming.*

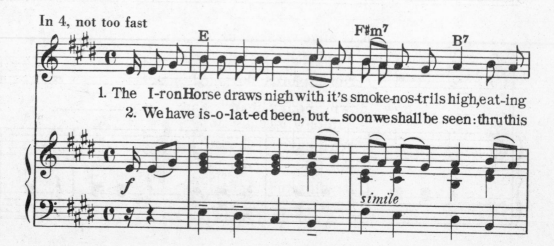

In 4, not too fast

1. The Iron Horse draws nigh with it's smoke-nos-trils high, eat-ing
2. We have is-o-lat-ed been, but soon we shall be seen: thru this

286.

fire while he graz-eth, drink-ing wa-ter while he blaz-eth; then the
White Moun-tain re-gion folks can learn of our re - li-gion. Count each

steam forc- es out, whis-tles loud clear the route, for the
man, man - y wives, how they're held in their hives, and

I - ron Horse is com-ing with a train in his wake.
see those dread-ful dives, how they lynch man - y lives.

3. If alive we shall be,
Many folks we shall see,
Nobles, lords, flotsam, beggars,
Among us will come the slavers.
Saints will come, sinners too.
We'll have all that we can do,
For this great Union Railroad
It will fetch the devil through.

# THE COWBOY'S LAMENT

Robert j Lee

*A variant of an Irish song, "The Unfortunate Rake."*

Waltz, rather slow

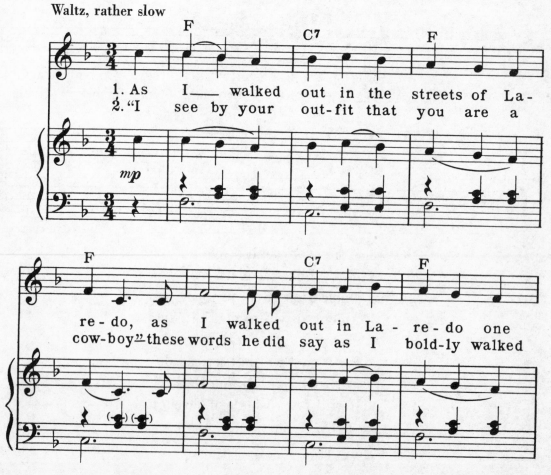

1. As I___ walked out in the streets of La-
2. "I see by your out-fit that you are a

re- do, as I walked out in La- re- do one
cow- boy" these words he did say as I bold- ly walked

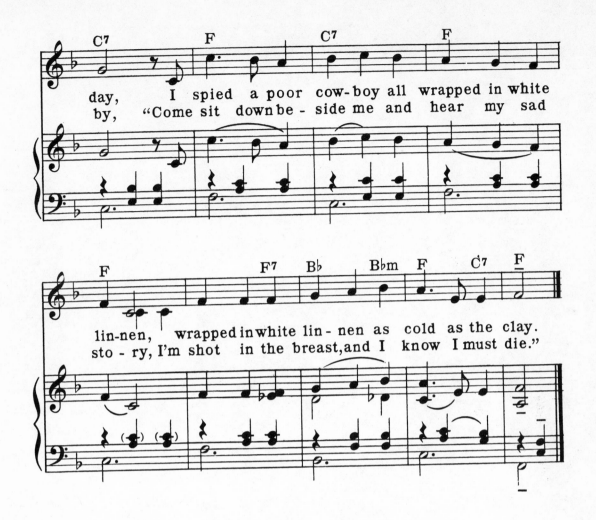

day,    I spied a poor cow-boy all wrapped in white
by,   "Come sit down be - side me and hear my sad

lin-nen,  wrapped in white lin-nen as cold as the clay.
sto - ry, I'm shot in the breast, and I know I must die."

3. "It was once in the saddle I used to go dashing,
   Once in the saddle I used to go gay,
   First down to Rosie's and then to the card house,
   Shot in the breast and I'm dying today.

4. "Get sixteen gamblers to carry my coffin
   Six purty maidens to sing me a song;
   Take me to the valley and lay the sod o'er me,
   For I'm a young cowboy an' know I done wrong.

5. "O, beat the drum slowly and play the fife lowly,
   Play the dead march as they carry me along,
   Put bunches of roses all over my coffin,
   Roses to deaden the clods as they fall."

6. As I walked out in the streets of Laredo,
   As I walked out in Laredo one day,
   I spied a young cowboy all wrapped in white linen,
   Wrapped in white linen, as cold as the clay.

# TITLE INDEX

# INDEX OF FIRST LINES

294

# BURL IVES Recordings on Decca Records

## FOLK SONG ALBUMS *(all records available as singles).*

### BALLADS & FOLK SONGS
### Volume I (DL 5080)

Dublin City
Cockle Shells
Old Dan Tucker
The Erie Canal
Eddystone Light
Hullabaloo-Belay
Venezuela
The Fox
Lolly-too-dum
Aunt Rhody
Saturday Night
Wake Nicodemus

### BALLADS & FOLK SONGS
### Volume II (DL 5013)

Turtle Dove
Devil's Nine Questions
No Wood Fire
Ten Thousand Miles
My Good Old Man
Po' Boy
I'm Sad and I'm Lonely
Down in the Valley
Cowboy's Lament

### BALLADS & FOLK SONGS
### Volume III (DL 5093)

Rodger Young
Foggy, Foggy Dew
Blue Tail Fly
I'm Goin' Down the Road
Big Rock Candy Mountain
It Makes No Difference Now
I'm Thinking Tonight of My Blue Eyes
Old Uncle Ned
On the Grand Canyon Line

### WOMEN: FOLK SONGS ABOUT
### THE FAIR SEX (DL 5490)

Liza Jane
Barbara Allen

The Woman and the Chivalrous Shark
The Wealthy Old Maid
(Warranty Deed)
My Pretty Little Miss
Devilish Mary
Molly Malone
Nellie McNess

### FOLK SONGS DRAMATIC AND
### HUMOROUS (DL 5467)

Git Along Little Dogies
From Here On Up The Hills
Don't Get Any Higher
The Golden Vanity
Hush Little Baby-Tibby Dunbar
I Know An Old Lady
Goober Peas
Old Bangham
Killegrew's Soiree
I Wonder As I Wander

### CHRISTMAS DAY IN
### THE MORNING (DL 5428)

TheSeven Joys of Mary
What Child Is This
There Were Three Ships
King Herod and the Cock
Down in Yon Forest
The Friendly Beasts
Jesus Ahatonia (Huron Indian Carol)

### ALBUMS FOR CHILDREN

1 (K 68) The Riddle Song
What Kind of Animal Are You?

2 (K 85) The Hen in the Hay
Mow
I Know an Old Lady

3 (K 107) Blue Tail Fly
Shoo Fly
Way Down Yonder in the Paw
Paw Patch

4 (K 106) Three Jolly Huntsmen
Let's Go Hunting

# BURL IVES Recordings on Columbia Records

## FOLK SONG ALBUMS *(all records available as singles)*.

### ALBUM 1—WAYFARING STRANGER
(CL 6109) (B 103) (C 103)

Darlin' Cory
Cotton-Eyed Joe
Cowboy's Lament (Streets of Laredo)
I Know My Love
I Know Where I'm Going
Leather-Winged Bat
On Top of Old Smokey
Peter Gray
Riddle Song
Sweet Betsy From Pike
Tam Pearce (Widdicomb Fair)
Wee Cooper O'Fife

### ALBUM 2—RETURN OF THE WAYFARING STRANGER
(CL 6058)

On Springfield Mountain
Little Mohee
Troubadour Song
Lord Randall
Bonnie Wee Lassie
Colorado Trail
John Hardy
Divil and the Farmer

### ALBUM 3—MORE FOLK SONGS
(CL 6144) (B 213)

High Barbaree
Pretty Polly
Pueblo Girl
Baby Did You Hear?
Old Blue
Ballandarie
Robin He Married
Lavendar Cowboy
I Got No Use For Women
Old Paint
Green Broom

### AMERICAN HYMNS
(CL 6115)

O Beulah Land
When I Get to the End of the Way

Fairest Lord Jesus
When the Roll is Called up Yonder
Forty Years Ago
Blessed Assurance
The Ninety and Nine
Beautiful Isle

### ALBUMS FOR CHILDREN:
### THE ANIMAL FAIR
(JL 8013) (J 459) (J 59)

The Grey Goose
Buckeye Jim
The Tailor and The Mouse
The Sow Took the Measles
Mr. Rabbit
The Whale

### MOTHER GOOSE SONGS
(J 467) (J 67)

Dickory, Dickory Dock
To Market, To Market
Pop Goes the Weasel
Little Jack Horner
Cock-a-Doodle Doo
Sing a Song of Sixpence
Hey Diddle Diddle
Three Blind Mice
Fiddle Dee Dee
Muffin Man
Pussy Cat

### SONGS NOT AVAILABLE IN ALBUMS: SINGLES ONLY

Wayfaring Stranger
Woolie Boogie Bee
Fooba-Wooba John
Two Little Owls
Down Back of the Barn
Where Have You Been?
Lollipop Tree
Two Little Trains
On Top of Old Smokey
Little White Duck

# BURL IVES Recordings for Encyclopaedia Britannica Films

*Historical America in Song*

## ALBUM 1, SONGS OF THE COLONIES

Psalm 3
Confess Jehovah
Mother Goose Songs
Little Mohee
The Tailor and the Mouse
Barbara Allen
Lord Thomas
Robin He Married
Lord Randall
The Bold Soldier
Edward
Black is the Color
The Squire's Son
The Riddle Song
Foggy, Foggy Dew
The Fox
Brennan on the Moor
Billy Boy
Queen Jane
Turtle Dove

## ALBUM II, SONGS OF THE REVOLUTION

The Escape of John Webb
I Know Where I'm Going
My Days Have Been So Wondrous Free
On Springfield Mountain
Chester
What a Court Hath Old England
Ballad of the Tea Party
The Boston Tea Tax
White Cockade
Free America
Johnny Has Gone for a Soldier
Yankee Doodle
Riflemen's Song at Bennington
The Battle of the Kegs
Ballad of Saratoga
Cornwallis Country Dance
Sir Peter Parker
Yankee Man O'War
Skip-to-my-Lou
Careless Love
Wayfaring Stranger

## ALBUM III, SONGS OF NORTH AND SOUTH

Ye Parliaments of England
The Constitution and the Guerriere
Patriotic Diggers
Hunters of Kentucky
The Hornet and the Peacock
Hey Betty Martin
Old Dan Tucker
Blue Tail Fly
The Abolitionist Hymn
Nicodemus
Old Abe Lincoln
All Quiet Along the Potomac Tonight
John Brown
Dixie
Bonnie Blue Flag
Goober Peas
The Battle of Bull Run
Johnny Comes Marching Home
Lorena
Kemo-Kimo
Beautiful Dreamer
Nobody Knows the Trouble I've Seen
Burying Ground
Were You There When They Crucified My Lord?

## ALBUM IV, SONGS OF THE SEA

Golden Vanity
High Barbaree
Maid of Amsterdam
Henry Martin
Hullabaloo Belay
Blow the Man Down
Blow Ye Winds
Away Rio
The Whale
Sacramento
Crocodile Song
Early in the Morning
Boston Come All Ye
Haul Away Joe
Venezuela
Shenandoah
Erie Canal
Eddystone Light

299

# BURL IVES Recordings for
## Encyclopaedia Britannica Films

ALBUM V, SONGS OF THE FRONTIER

Ox-Driving Song
Sweet Betsy from Pike
Dreary Black Hills
Peter Gray
Sioux Indians
Joe Bowers
What Was Your Name in the States?
Buffalo Gals
Greer County Bachelor
Roving Gambler
Chisholm Trail
Old Paint
Sod Shanty
Git Along Little Dogies
The Young Man Who Wouldn't
Hoe Corn
I've Got No Use For Women
The Hand-Cart Song
Brigham Young

ALBUM VI,
SONGS OF EXPANDING AMERICA

Streets of Laredo
Billy the Kid
John Hardy
Jesse James
Drill Ye Terriers
Blue Mountain Lake
Patrick on the Railroad
The Dying Hogger
John Henry
Down in the Valley
When I was Single
Sourwood Mountain
Cotton-Eye Joe
Cowboy's Dream
Life is Like a Mountain Railroad
Poor Boy
Old Blue
Midnight Special
Big Rock Candy Mountain
The Boll Weevil
St. John's River

*These records may be purchased from any EBF sales representative or directly from Encyclopaedia Britannica Films, 1150 Wilmette Avenue, Wilmette, Ill.*

# KEY TO THE GUITAR CHORDS
## Used in This Book

### BY HARRY VOLPE

• • • • • • • • • • • • • • • • • •

Each diagram represents the upper end of the finger-board towards the head of the guitar, as held in position for playing.

The six long vertical lines represent the six strings of the instrument, while the short vertical lines stand for frets.

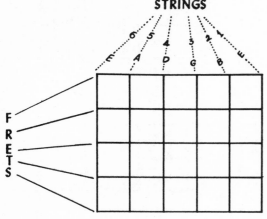

STRINGS

FRETS

● The large black dots designate places (behind the frets) where the strings are to be stopped to produce the notes.

(x) The small x represents a deadened string.

Left-hand fingers used are shown by small numerals below the diagram.

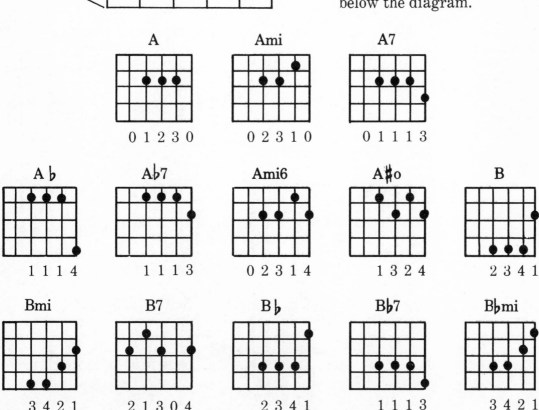

| A | Ami | A7 |
|---|---|---|
| 0 1 2 3 0 | 0 2 3 1 0 | 0 1 1 1 3 |

| A♭ | A♭7 | Ami6 | A♯o | B |
|---|---|---|---|---|
| 1 1 1 4 | 1 1 1 3 | 0 2 3 1 4 | 1 3 2 4 | 2 3 4 1 |

| Bmi | B7 | B♭ | B♭7 | B♭mi |
|---|---|---|---|---|
| 3 4 2 1 | 2 1 3 0 4 | 2 3 4 1 | 1 1 1 3 | 3 4 2 1 |

301

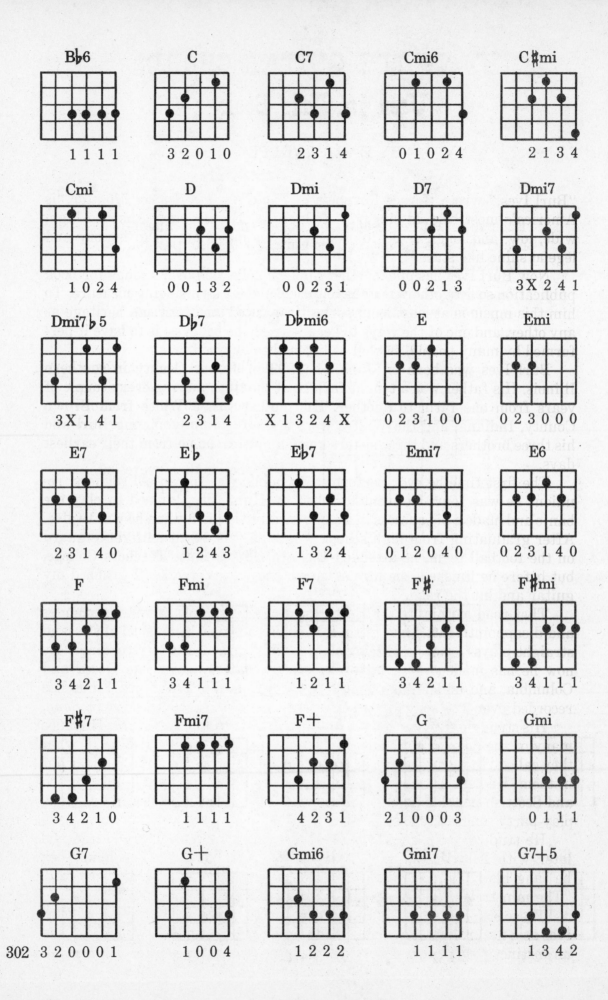

# ABOUT BURL IVES

"Burl Ives," wrote Horace Reynolds in *The Christian Science Monitor* "is America's most beloved singer of folk songs. He has sung America high, wide, low, and long . . . In his songs, he has made American history and legend shine like stars."

Now Burl Ives has put together his first collection of his songs for book publication so that others may have them for their own singing pleasure. To him this music is at least as important a part of the American heritage as any other, and one of the ways to keep it fresh, he believes, is to have it performed by many people, as well as listened to by them.

Burl Ives was born on June 14, 1909 in Jasper County in southern Illinois. His father was a tenant farmer at the time, moving every couple of years from one farm to another. His mother was a White from Brown County, Indiana, and the Whites were a singing family. Young Burl and his three brothers and three sisters knew a musical home from their earliest days.

The first time he ever performed in public was for an old soldiers' reunion; he was four. He went to school in Hunt City, learned to play the banjo and made a big success in a camp meeting in town when he was twelve. After graduating from high school, where he was an all-conference guard on the football team, he attended Eastern Illinois State Teachers College, but before he finished, the lure of music proved too strong. "I grabbed my guitar and hit the road."

That road led him to the East, through a long, hard series of struggles and disappointments, then to success on Broadway (in musical shows and straight plays), radio and television, movies, and of course recordings. By now he has made over a hundred records for companies like Decca and Columbia, and under the auspices of Encyclopaedia Britannica Films has recorded over 120 songs in a series entitled, *Historical America in Song.*

His struggle to make a place for himself as a ballad singer arose because many of the people in the entertainment world could see no value in what they called "those moss-covered songs." But Burl never faltered in his belief in them. He kept on collecting songs until he knew hundreds—old English and Scottish popular ballads, nursery songs, cowboy songs, railroad songs, play-party songs, work songs.

He studied voice, first with Madame Clara Lyon in Terre Haute and later with Ella Toedt; he learned acting from Benno Schneider. When he sang his ballads to Madame Toedt in her New York studio; she said, "The minstrels of old must have sung that way."

These studies of his are worth noting, for people tend to speak of Burl Ives as a natural, as if he had sprung up fully trained. But, while Burl had an instinct for singing which would not be denied, he worked hard on his songs after he got them. "I would change the words when I knew I had better ones," he says, in his autobiography, *Wayfaring Stranger*. "I would change the tune when I knew it would help the song." Often he spent weeks working on one song.

If you compare the songs he sings with the earliest versions of the same songs, you can get some idea not only of the work but of the genius it takes to make a great folk-song singer. Burl Ives' songs sound good because he makes them that way. He passes both words and tune through his personality, modifies them according to the dictates of his singing art. Many of the versions of these which we accept today are those which he has worked upon and, like the minstrels of old, given to the public.

Take a little thing; take the way he sings two lines of "The Foggy Foggy Dew." Most versions of this song run like this:

"I wooed her in the wintertime
And in the summer, too."

But Burl sings the second line, "Part of the summer, too." This bit of syncopation gives rhythmic excitement, a new spot of interest to the line. A small point, to be sure, but folk art is a frugal art, which gets large effects with small means.

Burl Ives, his wife, Helen, and their son, Alexander, live in an apartment in New York and on a ranch in California (when he's not on tour). He's a big man—six feet two, 245 pounds—and he likes racing his 46-foot boat, flying a plane and, as you might expect from a big man, food.

His whole large person and personality radiate with the vigor and warmth that international audiences have come to love and that glow through his autobiography, *Wayfaring Stranger*. This new collection of songs is in a sense the fruit of his experience and love of our music, passed on to the public, who can enjoy it and help to keep that music alive.